Noreen Riols

When Suffering Comes

To Joan,
affectionately
Noreen Riols.

Noreen Riols
When Suffering Comes

WORD PUBLISHING

WORD (UK) LTD
Milton Keynes, England

WORD AUSTRALIA
Kilsyth, Victoria, Australia

WORD COMMUNICATIONS LTD
Vancouver, B.C., Canada

STRUIK CHRISTIAN BOOKS (PTY) LTD
Maitland, South Africa

ALBY COMMERCIAL ENTERPRISES PTE LTD
Balmoral Road, Singapore

CHRISTIAN MARKETING NEW ZEALAND LTD
Havelock North, New Zealand

JENSCO LTD
Hong Kong

SALVATION BOOK CENTRE
Malaysia

WHEN SUFFERING COMES

ISBN 0-85009-321-X (Australian ISBN 1-86258-101-0)

Typeset by Suripace Ltd., Milton Keynes

Reproduced, printed and bound in Great Britain for Word (U.K.) Ltd by Richard Clay Ltd., Bungay

90 91 92 93 / 10 9 8 7 6 5 4 3 2 1

To

All Those

Who Are Hurting

Remember those who are suffering, as
though you were suffering as they are.
Hebrews 13v.3 (G.N.B.)

CONTENTS

PROLOGUE

> Why do I have to suffer?
> Why should this happen to me?
> Why does a loving God allow so much
> misery in the world?
> Why? ...... Why?

Who has not asked these and many similar questions when faced with physical pain, emotional turmoil, spiritual doubt, family upheavals, professional problems or disappointments? Although thousands of books have been written and studies undertaken on these eternal questions by theologians, doctors, psychologists, novelists, poets and countless others, the subject has been an issue since Adam's failure to resist temptation and will continue to be one for as long as men and women walk this earth.

As a nurse, as a wife and as a mother I, too, have known pain and witnessed deep suffering: I too have asked myself these agonising questions, often in the darkest hours of the night. For a very long time the question marks remained but, after years of groping and seeking, when I least expected it I found not AN answer, but THE answer. And my hope and prayer is that, as I recount some of the lessons God has taught me the hard way about suffering, those who are hurting as they read these pages will also find that answer.

The book is set in a large London teaching hospital where I trained as a nurse shortly after the war. Let me reassure the reader that it is not a veteran's story extolling the 'good old days' although it emphasises how greatly not only hospital rules and routine but society itself have altered in the intervening years. I hope it may also show that the rigidity of our training, far from expressing an apparent frustrated negativity, reflected a sense of discipline, a devotion to duty and a selflessness which has greatly benefited me ever since. These pages may perhaps be thought-provoking in this less formal, more relaxed age when the 'me first' concept sometimes tends to prevail.

Rules may change, society may change, the world may change – and the lifestyle and discipline of my old hospital have certainly changed – but the suffering and deep hurts in the hearts of human beings have not changed. We are still faced with the ever-present problem of how to cope when suffering comes...

CHAPTER ONE

The Old Lodge

The rain which had been threatening all morning had blown over before the train left London. But when it stopped at the small country station a soft spring shower was pattering gently against the compartment's dirty windows.

I stepped down onto the almost deserted platform, looking around for the exit. I appeared to be the only passenger alighting but suddenly, almost as if she hadn't realised she had arrived, a young woman threw open a carriage door and jumped hurriedly down, dragging a heavy suitcase after her.

The guard blew his whistle, the train snorted and slowly began to move away as we two, the only passengers to get off, walked towards the ticket collector hunched in his little box at the entrance.

"Can you tell me where I can get a taxi?" I enquired of him, seeing no sign of life in the country road outside the station.

"Where d'you want to go lady?" he asked.

"The Old Lodge," I replied.

"Call Charlie," he shouted to a young porter who was pushing an empty barrow along the platform.

"Lady wants to go to the Old Lodge."

"It'll be 'ere in a minute," the ticket collector said without showing much interest, retiring to his high stool inside the dreary cubby-hole.

The woman who had left the train so hastily came up beside me.

"I'm going to the Old Lodge too," she said diffidently. "Do you think I could share your cab?"

I looked at her and my heart sank.

She was older than me, nearer thirty, with a well-scrubbed face, good sensible shoes and wispy mouse-coloured hair escaping from under the brim of her shapeless felt hat. Just the sort of person I had dreaded meeting at the Old Lodge.

"By all means," I answered coldly as an old rather dirty motor slid up beside us and a red-faced man in dungarees, who looked as if he'd just come from underneath the car, stepped out and jerked open the boot.

"New intake?" he enquired, his home-made cigarette, which was stuck to his upper lip, waggling up and down as he spoke.

"Yes," I replied, getting into the back seat as my companion climbed in beside me.

"Car's been going up and down the 'ill for the last hour," he announced as we drove away from the station. "I took up four who came in on the two thirty. I expect you two'll be among the last to arrive."

I didn't reply.

"I DO hope we're not late," my companion said nervously. "I had MEANT to arrive on the two thirty but the tube was so slow."

"They'll wait," I said drily. "We're here for three months so I don't suppose half an hour matters much either way."

She looked at me in surprise and I could sense that she didn't know what to reply, what to make of me: that she was a little frightened of me and, oddly enough, her diffidence gave me strength, even added an aggressive touch to my own growing apprehension. And I didn't want to put her at ease, didn't want to say soothing encouraging words, but was almost comforted by her discomfort. It was as if we were on a see-saw with me sitting at the top: I knew that if I lowered my end, my defences, before her apprehension, I would be let down sharply and the latent fear at the dramatic change which was about to take place in my life, and which up to this moment I had pushed to the back of my mind, would leap up and engulf me.

And so we sat together in an embarrassed silence.

"I'm Agnes Braithwaite," she ventured at last.

"How do you do," I replied without showing any great

interest, mentally adding: I might have guessed. Her name typified her, plain and old-fashioned. Never by any wild stretch of the imagination could she have been taken for a Lucinda or a Drusilla.

She shifted uncomfortably, obviously sensing my indifference.

"Do you know this area?" she went on, desperate to cover up the icy silence between us.

It would have been so easy for me to break it with a reassuring smile, to put her at ease, but my spirits had suddenly sunk to zero and not only had I no desire to smile but I was afraid, afraid that my defence mechanism might collapse and allow her to trample across the barrier which I had erected between us.

"Not terribly well," I replied.

"I come from Cheshire," she volunteered. "I've lived at home until now. This is my first real venture alone."

I looked at her incredulously and couldn't believe what I had just heard: couldn't believe that anyone of her age who had lived through the war could have had such a sheltered existence.

"And now you've ventured, do you regret it?" I asked, a touch of sarcasm in my voice.

She smiled hesitantly, but only with her lips. Her eyes did not smile and I sensed her lurking fear.

"No, not really," she answered slowly.

She paused again.

"I'm an only child," she went on at last, looking straight ahead of her at the back of Charlie's head. "My mother died when I was eight and since then there's only been my father and me."

She paused again and her eyes left Charlie's head and travelled downwards to her shoes. For one horrible moment I thought she was going to burst into tears and I almost panicked. I couldn't cope with that sort of emotion at the moment. But she didn't and after taking a deep breath, which might have been a sigh, she went on.

"He had a stroke nine years ago which left him paralysed: I helped to nurse him till he died last July."

Charlie cursed as he swerved the car to avoid a young cyclist and she and I were momentarily thrown against each other. She looked straight at me but there were no tears in her pale blue eyes, just an immense sadness.

"I feel now that I want to put into practice what I learned during those nine years, so that it won't be wasted," she ended.

"Very worthy," I said, looking straight ahead of me, and hated myself even more. How could I be so disagreeable to this pathetic, vulnerable creature? But I still made no attempt, no effort to break the even more uncomfortable silence which now hovered between us.

"Just running into the drive ladies," Charlie threw out over his shoulder.

He half-turned in our direction and I could see the unlighted cigarette still dangling perilously from his upper lip.

"After this next bend you'll see the 'ouse," he added. "Just be'ind that large bush. Proper 'ive of activity it is this afternoon."

'That large bush' turned out to be the most enormous clump of rhododendrons I had ever seen and I could just imagine what a magnificent display there would be in a few weeks' time when it would be ablaze with hundreds of multi-coloured blooms.

As I turned and looked out through the rain-spattered window I heard her voice again.

"Why did YOU decide to come?" she enquired gently.

I continued to stare stonily through the car window. Her question had raised an unanswered question in my own mind, touched a raw spot which I had preferred to ignore until that moment.

"I don't know," I replied at last without turning round.

And, at that moment, I truly didn't.

******

As we swung round the bend the lovely old house came into view. Suitcases, trunks, travel bags and hat boxes were piled everywhere and young women were milling round under the huge overhanging porch saying goodbye to parents or dragging tennis racquets and other paraphernalia from the boots of cars.

Charlie slowed to a standstill before this seeming chaos and a thin woman in nurse's uniform stepped from under the porch and opened the car door. Her hair was iron grey, in places white, and drawn up into a soft bun beneath her delicate muslin cap. But her face, which was devoid of make-up, was young and unlined.

"She looks like a hen," I said drily, determined at that moment to hate everything.

My travelling companion giggled nervously.

But then the nurse smiled.

She had looked tense and worried as she opened the door but suddenly as the smile broke out her whole expression changed.

"Welcome to the Old Lodge," she said warmly as we stepped down into the damp freshness of the spring afternoon. "Don't bother with your cases, Charlie will carry them through into the hall."

The taxi driver was obviously well known at the house.

"Go straight through into the drawing room and have tea. I expect you're ready for a cup after the journey."

And she turned away as another car drew up behind us.

Charlie swung our heavy cases out of the boot and carried them easily into the large oak-panelled hall.

"'ere we are Sister," he announced. "Another couple to add to the list."

The Sister seated behind the large desk was younger and prettier than the nurse who had greeted us. She dimpled as she smiled up at our chauffeur.

"Put them down there Charlie, with the others." Turning to us she said, "When you've had tea come back to me and I'll give you your room numbers. Don't be too long, we want you all in the classroom, in uniform, by five."

And she turned to greet a young girl who had just walked in, flanked on either side by her parents.

I wandered across the hall and into the drawing room

from where a steady buzz of conversation and the tinkle of china came as a horde of young women poured themselves tea from a large pot: it was obvious that many of them already knew each other and, as I had done with my companion in the taxi, I instinctively pulled in my antennae and drew away.

It was all too much like a schoolgirl gathering in the common room after the hols and not at all what I had expected.

I don't really know what I HAD expected, but certainly not to be catapulted into this jolly hockeysticks atmosphere. Having been told to arrive on Saturday afternoon I had vaguely imagined that we would have had a lazy country house weekend in front of us, giving everyone time to relax and get to know each other before starting in earnest on Monday morning: not this frenzied rush into the classroom.

And I suddenly realised that the answer I had given my companion in the taxi, when she had asked me why I was here, was the right one. At the time I had wanted to be provocative, but it was the truth after all. I really did not know what had possessed me, what had pushed me into dropping everything and deciding at the age of twenty-four, against all the rational, well thought-out arguments of my family, to go and train as a nurse at one of London's most famous teaching hospitals. My sophisticated friends were stunned: to abandon our carefree, happy-go-lucky lifestyle for nursing could only mean one thing – that I had been dropped on my head when young and the after-effects were only just beginning to surface!

I had survived the war, not without scars, followed by an interesting job with the Overseas Services of the BBC, reputed at that time to be one of the best clubs in London. Like most young women in the immediate post-war years, I had enjoyed an exciting, at times frenetic, social life. A spate of captivating American musicals were filling the theatres to capacity in the mid-forties and setting us all humming. FUN, with a capital F, had broken out like a rash all over London, and those of us who had survived attempted, with frenzied gaiety, to push broken hearts and painful memories into our subconscious and pretend they hadn't happened.

But the previous summer everything had inexplicably gone dull and soured on me. Hunt Balls, Regimental Balls, point-to-point meetings, tea at Gunters, dancing at the Mirabelle or the Café de Paris to the sentimental lilting music of Geraldo or Mantovani or the throbbing beat of Edmundo Ros and his Rumba Band had suddenly lost their charm and seemed pointless. And I had begun to ask myself: Why am I here? What's life all about?

And I didn't have the answer.

I knew that I had to find an outlet, another career, something which would help me deal with that nagging question. But another question posed itself. What?

As I stood there apart from the laughing group of girls who all looked so young, I remembered my father's words when I announced that I had decided to train as a nurse.

"You won't last the first year," he had laughed.

My mother had said nothing and I didn't know which was the more difficult to cope with, her silence or my father's amusement.

"But if you must do this mad thing," he continued, "at least do it properly. Train at the best hospital although, of course, they may not accept you; there's always a very long waiting list."

Perhaps when I applied, the novelty was already beginning to wear off and I had rather hoped they would NOT accept me; that would have been my loophole. But they did and I had been caught in the net of my pride and bravado, refusing to admit that I wasn't entirely sure I had made the right decision.

I put down my cup and walked back to the desk in the hall. The Sister looked up from her lists as I gave her my name.

"Straight up the stairs, left at the top, along the corridor and turn right. Your room is the second on the left: you'll see your name on the door."

She paused.

"You've been to Daniel Neal's and bought your shoes, I hope?"

I nodded.

"Two pairs?" she queried.

I nodded again.

"Be sure to alternate them. Never wear the same pair two days running: your feet are crucial in this profession."

She glanced at the old grandfather clock ticking solemnly in a dark corner of the hall.

"You won't have time to do much unpacking now," she ended. "It'll have to wait till after supper. Just change into your uniform and go straight to the classroom."

"Where…?" I began.

"Come back down here and follow the crowd."

She smiled, sensing my bewilderment.

"Everyone else is in the same boat. They none of them know where anything is, but you'll soon find out."

And she picked up her pen and went back to her lists.

I wished she had said 'soon be at home', it would have made me feel more comfortable, less ill at ease. But I realised that this was business and we weren't meant to feel at home. We were here to train and to work. Just how hard, I was soon to find out.

CHAPTER TWO

Marching Orders

I followed the crowd, as she had advised me, and at the end of a long dark corridor entered a classroom where I saw the Braithwaite girl sitting alone at a two-seater desk, looking lost and pathetic. She glanced up and smiled appealingly at me as I came in, obviously feeling as alone as I did and pleading with her eyes for me to take the seat beside her.

But her helplessness irritated me and I pretended not to see her as, self-conscious in the unattractive old-fashioned uniform and sensible high-laced shoes, the like of which I hadn't worn since my schooldays and had vowed never to wear again, I meandered down the aisle.

Most of the desks were already occupied and a feeling of panic gripped me: everyone but Agnes Braithwaite and me appeared to know each other and to be chatting happily. How was I going to cope? And again the question loomed large in my mind. What AM I doing here? What madness had propelled me to take such a crazy decision, to give up my social whirl, my independent London life, even the smart cherry-coloured suit with the black velvet collar which I had been wearing when I arrived, for this shapeless striped cotton dress with the uncomfortable stiff white collar fastened with men's studs which I had found so difficult to manipulate, and the black granny shoes which now squeaked on my feet?

What? What indeed!

The answer was only to come many years later when I looked back on my life and saw the way the different strands had been woven together by some unseen hand to form a pattern. But, at that moment, I felt I had lost all identity.

It had been a shock to find my room and see NURSE Baxter neatly printed on a card on the door. And then to discover that starched white apron and uniform dress laid out for me on the bed. The only redeeming feature was the frilly little muslin cap and I had spent precious minutes fixing my hair in an attractive halo around it, which was why I had been one of the last to arrive and find the classroom almost full. I would have so much preferred to get there early enough to install myself in one of the two-seater desks and ignore whoever chose to sit beside me.

As the instinct to run rose up inside me again, my dress was twitched and I looked down to see a plump, smiling girl with a pert, upturned nose and an impish face.

"There's no one sitting here," she volunteered, sliding along the form behind her desk.

I sat down. There didn't seem to be anything else to do.

Suddenly a hush fell over everything and a Sister I had not yet met swept majestically into the room and, as she motioned us to stand, we rose as one body, awed by her presence. Had she been the Queen she could not have inspired greater reverence in us all at that moment.

She was beautiful, with perfect features and prematurely white hair framing her face like a Madonna. But there was not the gentleness one sees in portraits of the Madonna: her eyes were grey and steely and, as well as a look of authority, they revealed a certain hardness.

"Sit down nurses," she said pleasantly and proceeded to belie her kindly tones by telling us in no uncertain terms just what was expected of us.

"You will soon get to know each other," she went on and I felt slightly comforted.

The girl sitting beside me was drawing laughing cats on the sheet of paper in front of her and, seeing them, I relaxed. She looked at me and her large blue eyes twinkled. The cat she had just sketched had stopped laughing and bore a striking resemblance to the Sister. I pursed my lips trying not to laugh and realised that I had missed the Sister's last words.

"...... but you will address each other either as nurse or by your surnames. In no circumstances are Christian names to be used."

Shock number one.

I looked down: the last cat on the page had started to cry and was rubbing its eyes pathetically with a furry paw.

She continued to give us a further series of jolts disguised as 'you wills' until I thought I had made a mistake and unknowingly joined the women's branch of the French Foreign Legion! The cats obviously thought so too!

As these shock waves tumbled through my mind, out of the corner of my eye I noticed that the last cat had recovered from its weeping fit and was now standing stiffly at the salute wearing a policeman's helmet. I giggled as, under my companion's deft pen, puss raised his truncheon and began bludgeoning a howling prostrate nurse from whose gaping mouth a 'help' bubble was billowing.

"And now nurses," Sister's voice once again broke in on my wandering thoughts, "you will proceed in an orderly fashion to the practical room: nurses must NEVER hurry or appear flustered WHATEVER the circumstances."

I breathed a sigh of relief. At last we were getting down to the real thing and I mentally rubbed my hands in anticipation, already seeing myself as the 20th century Florence Nightingale, only to have my hopes extinguished by her next words.

"Nurse Thomas is waiting for you." She paused and there was an almost malicious glint in her beautiful eyes. "She is going to show you how to sweep a floor."

I began to feel like a ping pong ball being batted backwards and forwards as these successive blows kept hitting me from every direction.

"SWEEP A FLOOR," I gasped in unbelief. "Is THIS what I gave up my freedom for? To be shown how to sweep a floor!"

The words thundered inside me and my whole body bristled with indignation inside my stiff white apron as I resentfully followed the meek, schoolgirl crowd out of the classroom and down the passage.

ANY fool can sweep a floor, I hissed angrily to myself.

But I soon discovered, with the expert help of Nurse Thomas, that any fool can indeed sweep a floor, and up till that moment I had been one of those fools, but to do it properly was quite another thing.

"There is a right and a wrong way to sweep a floor," Nurse Thomas, the one whom I'd earlier described as a hen, explained kindly, "a hygienic and an unhygienic way."

And as we gathered around her, everyone but me seemingly agog with excitement and bursting to know more, she wielded a broom and proceeded to demonstrate that up till then most, if not all, of us had been doing it the unhygienic way.

After this startling revelation, we were taught how to scour a sink, hot-dust the tops of bedside lockers, and scrub dirty sheets and other unspeakably soiled bed linen with nothing but a long-handled broom and an abundant supply of cold running water: how to carry out, in fact, all the menial tasks which it had never occurred to me that a nurse, or for that matter any enlightened woman of my generation, was ever called upon to perform.

Had I been told then that I would spend my first year at the hospital doing just that, I think I would have bolted on that very first day.

But mercifully I was spared a glimpse into my future and imagined that all this scouring and spit and polish was only part of the initial three months' training, just to keep us busy and out of mischief until we had live bodies to practise upon: and that as soon as we were transferred to London, to the hospital proper and 'on the wards', I would indeed be soothing the fevered brows of groaning patients and sweeping majestically along dimly-lit corridors with my lamp held high.

As we abandoned our assortment of floor-cloths, mops and brooms and prepared to answer the supper bell, Sister dealt us her final few blows.

"I notice that some of you are wearing your hair far too long for tidiness... and cleanliness," she began. "If this applies to you, pin it into a bun and tuck it under your cap out of sight before you come back to the classroom after supper."

AFTER SUPPER!

It couldn't be true. Were we expected to spend our entire Saturday evening doing even more communal charring?

I surreptitiously put a hand up to my collar.

It was starched and stiff, rather like those worn by young men in Edwardian photographs, and I felt a lone curl dangling perilously near the out of bounds area. In order not to be singled out as untidy or unhygienic I bent my head forward stiffly hoping the curl would retract and sat upright, looking no doubt as if I'd just been shot in the neck but was too polite to mention the fact.

"And from now on whenever you are in uniform you will not smoke," she continued. "The smell clings to your clothes and is very unpleasant for your patients."

I had never been anything more than a 'social' smoker but, like most young women of the early post-war era, I had a splendid silver cigarette case with my initials engraved on the flap which I enjoyed displaying. But, as her words sank in, I had a sudden unbearable desire to light up, so much so that I almost missed her next volley.

"Neither will you wear any kind of make-up."

An audible gasp went round the room and, hearing it, she let a smile play round the corners of her mouth. There was something of the actress in her and I wasn't entirely convinced that she wasn't enjoying the successive waves of misery which seemed to be sweeping over us all.

She paused dramatically and I had the feeling that we were mentally bracing ourselves for whatever disaster was about to strike us next.

"Not even face powder," she said, enunciating the words clearly, one by one.

By now the initial glum silence was almost defiant, and I wondered why we didn't all just get up and walk out.

But no one moved.

I began to lick nervously at the cherry-coloured lipstick I was wearing which I had chosen so carefully to exactly match my suit. My nails were the same colour and I clenched my fists hoping desperately that no one had noticed, waves of guilt sweeping over me at the thought of being revealed as such a Jezebel.

"And as for nail varnish..." Her steely grey eyes seemed to be looking straight at me, but I knew it was only my imagination as other feet were now shifting uncomfortably.

Then she smiled and this time the hardness had disappeared from her eyes and they were twinkling. It was almost as if she were saying, 'I understand what you're feeling: I haven't forgotten what it's like to be young: I've been there in your place but don't worry, you'll survive!'

"There's nothing wrong with make-up," she said kindly, and there was an almost visible release of tension in the room. "But there's nothing more unsightly than make-up which is stale and beginning to wear off. When you are working on the wards you are all going to be very busy."

She paused.

"I wonder if you realise just HOW busy," she said softly, "and you won't have time to keep doing up your faces. Perfume, even the slight whiff from face powder, can be nauseating to a patient who is already feeling sick."

I hadn't thought of that, but it was true.

"The same applies to your nail varnish. Coloured finger nails can hide dirt, so keep your nails short, trimmed and unvarnished so that no germs can lodge underneath."

No one said a word. I don't think any of us would have dared to challenge what she said, let alone disagree with her.

She motioned to the girl sitting nearest the door, who immediately leapt from her seat and triumphantly opened it.

"NO Nurse," Sister said testily, "NOT like that."

And as she glided noiselessly across the room and demonstrated how to open and close a door without so much as a gentle click being heard, we all jumped to our feet as if activated by a hidden spring.

She was that sort of person.

******

By nine o'clock the day's cleaning sessions were finally over and we were dismissed.

I wandered back to the drawing room, now slightly thawed inside and more relaxed, hoping for a little company: but the room was in darkness. I switched on the light and went over to the fireplace: the ashes were grey and dead in the grate and the room which had been so cheerful just a few hours ago was now cold and uninviting, so that my spirits dropped to the same temperature.

There appeared to be nothing left to do but go to bed. At nine o'clock on a Saturday evening! I hadn't been to bed that early since I left school and I felt lonely, lost and cheated.

My mind wandered back to Saturday evenings in my old home and on an impulse I almost rang my parents, just to have someone to talk to, but then decided against it. My voice might betray me and anyway, what could I say? "It's absolutely ghastly. I've made a dreadful mistake. It's worse than being at school again, worse than anything I ever imagined."

What was the point?

My parents couldn't do anything about it and it had been my decision after all, not theirs.

I turned away from the empty grate and flicked off the light, then slowly climbed the wide staircase and opened the door to my little room.

It was none too warm.

The rambling old house must have been unheatable at the best of times but now with fuel rationing down to its bare minimum it was unlikely that it would ever be really comfortable. I decided that the only thing to do was to go to bed. Climbing out of the stiff, unattractive uniform I picked up my towel and went along to the bathrooms at the other end of the corridor, but they were both occupied and, judging from the splashing noises coming from inside, their occupants weren't in any hurry to come out.

As I retraced my steps and shut the door of my little cell behind me I dropped to my knees by the side of the high narrow bed and mechanically began to recite the Lord's Prayer, a nightly ritual I had performed ever since I stopped chanting 'Gentle Jesus, meek and mild', the prayer my mother had taught me to say almost as soon as I could talk.

But halfway through I suddenly stopped.

What was I saying? What did it all mean? That nagging question – What's it all about? – had come dancing into my mind again.

I leant back on my heels and looked up at the bare ceiling from which the glaring electric bulb dangled, but no flash of light, no inspiration, no answer came. Not that I really expected one, and I began to wonder whether God was not just one giant hoax, whether one day I would wake up to discover that there was no one there after all. And for the first time in many years I got up from my knees without asking this unknown God to bless and watch over each member of my family. There somehow didn't seem to be any point in it any more.

As I climbed wearily and somewhat dejectedly into my cold hard bed and rolled over to switch off the light, in the stillness I heard the sound of heart-rending sobs coming from the room next door.

CHAPTER THREE

Turning a Page

A hard metallic screeching tore into my sleep, jerking me awake.

For a few seconds I lay in the unfamiliar bed bewildered and lost, not remembering where I was, till my eyes fell on the nurse's dress I had worn for the first time the day before, draped across the hard-backed chair, and the pretty frilly muslin cap with its butterfly bow sitting coyly on the dressing table.

As consciousness slowly seeped like a receding mist back into my mind the screeching gradually died away and I recognised the sound of an electric bell shrilling harshly through the gracious old house.

My room was bathed in a cold eerie twilight, a thin filter of grey creeping under the curtains at the high window. Turning lazily over and squinting at my watch I realised that my little cell must be north facing and could give no indication of what the spring morning was really like.

I lay there, my hands clasped behind my head, remembering. Remembering other Sunday mornings when I had been awakened in my room at home by the early morning sunlight pouring in through the closed chintz curtains, sending sunbeams dancing onto the walls or creeping up from the foot of my bed. Sunny spring mornings when my younger brother and I had so often gone riding across the downs, returning exhausted with the exercise, exhilarated by the fresh air, the flying landscape all around us and the feel of the sharp sea wind on our faces as we galloped for mile after mile.

And the tranquil lazy afternoons when we had slumbered contentedly in front of the drawing room fire, surrounded by the Sunday papers.

I wondered whether there would be any Sunday papers today. Or, if there were, whether we would have time to read them. And with a pang of self-pity I realised that for the next three months this dark sunless room would be the only place to which I could escape when the pressure of a horde of women became too much.

I heard the door next to mine open and close quietly and the sound of light footsteps, and I wondered about the person who was my neighbour and whose heart-rending sobs I had heard on the other side of the wall the night before. It had not been the crying of a homesick young girl but rather the deep, harsh, almost tearless weeping of a woman whose heart was breaking.

But doors were beginning to bang and other footsteps echo in the corridor outside. I gathered that it was time to get up, time to face whatever the day had in store.

Mercifully hot water flowed into the washbowl, set in a corner of the room, as I turned on the tap and splashed my face. And I suddenly laughed. How different all this was turning out to be from what I had imagined. I had only seen the romantic side of hospital training, the motion picture slant, not the grim reality of coping day in and day out with seemingly petty rules and regulations. And almost before I had even begun to circle the periphery, I asked myself whether I would manage to stay the course: yet again what had even motivated me to try. Surely the sudden emptiness I had felt during the preceding months, which had led me to apply to the nursing school, was preferable to this dreadful regimentation, leaping to the harsh sound of bells, cold cell-like rooms, no make-up, no time off and, as far as I could see, nothing but endless crushing submission to autocratic authority, all to be accepted with downcast eyes and without protest. And a sudden anger bubbled up inside me.

"I didn't apply to enter a convent," I muttered, rubbing the rough white hospital towel across the back of my neck.

Then my sense of humour surfaced as an amusing thought crossed my mind.

"I wonder if they'll check whether we've washed our necks!"

I grimaced at my face reflected back at me from the mirror.

Another bell sounded shrilly and, hurriedly fixing my cap into position, not bothering this time to drape my hair becomingly above my shiny nose, I ran from the room and down the stairs.

I must have been one of the last to enter the dining room. The Sisters were all there and the one who had given us so many 'don't's the evening before nodded curtly as I slipped behind the nearest chair, waiting with the others for her to offer thanks for the meal we were about to share.

A subdued hum of chatter broke out as chairs were scraped back and thick white cups were passed along to the end of the table to be filled with tea.

I have always hated thick china, especially for tea, but at that moment I think I hated everything and had we been served from a Georgian silver teapot into Royal Doulton cups I'm sure I would have felt just the same. I made no attempt to talk to the girls sitting on either side of me, but I don't think they even noticed. They continued chatting animatedly together, seemingly thrilled with all that they had so far experienced, leaving me in my self-imposed solitude to wallow in self-pity as I spread marmalade onto thick slices of bread and margarine.

My melancholy nature delved into the past and I realised that a page had definitely turned not only for me but for my whole family.

Only the month before, on St. Valentine's Day, my brother had left to join his regiment in Malaya: and I thought back to that cold bright February afternoon when my parents and I had lunched with Geoffrey before he caught the boat train to Southampton. Waterloo Station had been teeming with soldiers as drafts from several regiments on their way to combat zones in Korea or Malaya were embarking on the same troopship. I could still see twitching tartan trews, swinging kilts and the jaunty green berets of an Irish regiment bobbing above the crowd as the soldiers were marched through the station to board the waiting train.

The animated conversation at the table ebbed and

flowed around me. I remembered how excited Geoffrey had been as the time for his departure drew nearer: and I had shared his enthusiasm. His future had seemed to me to be opening on to thrilling new adventure. Yet, when the guard finally blew his whistle and the train, crammed with soldiers, crawled slowly away from the platform, my mother had said nothing.

But now sitting in the bare sunlit dining room reminiscing, I began to wonder just what had gone through her mind, what she had felt as she watched her only son, a young twenty-year-old subaltern not long out of Sandhurst, go off to fight a cruel war in a steamy, dense, malaria-infested Malayan jungle.

And as I sat alone in the midst of this buzzing chatter, I saw the whole scene in a different light and knew that I was feeling as she must have felt, alone in a crowd on that noisy echoing station. And suddenly the excitement which had filled me at Waterloo that February afternoon evaporated, and it all seemed absurd: life seemed absurd. My mother only had two children and now one had gone off to fight and possibly to kill and the other to try to heal and preserve life. Once again I felt I was on the tip of a perilous see-saw which could let me down with a bump at any minute.

And that same haunting question waltzed tantalisingly into my mind. Why are we here? What's the point? What's it all about?

But a small handbell at the Sisters' table announcing that breakfast was over broke in on my ruminating.

Madonna, as I had irreverently nicknamed her, stood up.

"Your morning duties have been assigned to you," she announced as if she were reading out the list of the Queen's birthday honours. "You will find them on the notice-board in the hall. Sister, ..." she added, pointing to the dimpled young woman who had been behind the desk when we arrived, and my irritation mounted still further. Couldn't she give the poor girl a name? "...will help you with any queries you may have, but I think you should now know where to find everything."

She paused.

"Be in the large drawing room, wearing clean aprons, by eleven thirty for the morning service."

We all once again sprang to our feet as if there were fire crackers under our seats, as she swept from the room.

I stood on the edge of the press of women crowding eagerly round the notice-board, hoping that I had been given flowers to arrange or a little gentle dusting. But when I got nearer I saw that I had been appointed to scour and clean all the baths and washbowls.

My once soft white hands were already beginning to show signs of wear from the previous evening's encounter with cold water and scrubbing brush and I was tempted to ask one of those who had been favoured with sweeping to swop jobs. But none of the names meant anything to me. As I turned miserably away, I caught sight of Braithwaite. She waved happily in my direction as she scurried off in search of pails, mops and washcloths, seemingly blissfully content with whatever ghastly task had been assigned to her.

When I returned to my room a couple of hours later to change my now soiled and crumpled apron I wondered how on earth I was going to survive the next few months of hard labour with what threatened to be gaping red sores around my knuckles.

As we assembled in the large drawing room, the mist of faces was beginning to divide and form separate identities and I realised that, in spite of myself, I knew one or two names besides Braithwaite's. The sandy-haired Scottish girl who had vigorously helped me with the bath scouring was called Donaldson and the one whom I had sat next to in the classroom the evening before was Johnson. As each face detached itself from the crowd they started to look less like the huddle of penguins they'd appeared to be the evening before, clustered together in obedient ranks with two black shod feet sticking out from beneath their long white aprons.

In spite of my resistance life was beginning to form a pattern as we all congregated in that spacious room which looked out onto a wide terrace with manicured lawns beyond.

Sister swept majestically in once again and dropped to

her knees in front of a small reading desk on which an open Bible had been placed. Not knowing what was expected of us we all followed suit and the short service began.

Little did I know it then but I had already set my feet on the path I would follow for the next four years, working as a student nurse in the hospital itself. Every morning and evening when the first of Big Ben's eight chimes rang across London a deep silence would fall over that vast hospital as in every ward Sisters and nurses dropped to their knees and asked God's blessing on the day or night which lay ahead.

Looking back I realise now how these moments of absolute stillness must have had a calming effect on those who were facing the future with apprehension, waiting for an operation or a doctor's diagnosis which they had reason to fear might not be a happy one.

But this was in the future and as, after the first few days, a pattern of what life as a student nurse meant slowly began to emerge, the regular rhythm, the security of routine took hold of me and I started to look back with less and less nostalgia for the life which I had left behind. And which, I forgot to remind myself in my moments of overwhelming self-pity, I had willingly, and against most people's good advice, given up.

I didn't know why I had given it up. I didn't know why I had been propelled into this totally different world from the one I had known and it was many years before I was to discover the answer. At that time I believed in God because I had been brought up to do so, to go to church, to say my prayers at night. But God was a habit to me, like cleaning my teeth. I didn't believe in a LIVING God, one who really heard me when I prayed, one who could and would answer me if I just took the time to listen. A God who had a perfect plan for my life.

Yet as I look back, I now understand that although He in no way forced me to accept this plan or pushed me into this different lifestyle, He was there all the time guiding me. I wasn't in any way obliged to accept His guidance but mercifully, without realising it, I did. And as He helped me along this new path He gradually opened up before me riches and depths of happiness and sorrow as the different stages of my life unfolded beneath His protective hand.

CHAPTER FOUR

Roddy Never Knew

It wasn't until the end of the week that I discovered the identity of my neighbour. I had been curious about her ever since that first evening when I had heard her sobbing in the darkness. But since I left getting up until the last minute and her door always clicked open very early, sometimes even before the bell screeched us into consciousness, we never crossed paths on the way to breakfast. And so I missed her, arriving in the dining room by a hair's breadth every morning, just in time to drop to my knees as the old grandfather clock chimed the hour.

I wondered why she got up so early, wasting precious time when she could have been sleeping, soaking up reserves for the day's battle with scrubbing brushes and brooms, followed by harrowing sessions in the classroom with an assortment of muscles and bones and sinews which we were all desperately trying to assimilate. Some of the younger girls were getting quite hysterical about the amount of information on the human body which we were expected to master, wailing that they would never make the grade in the short time allowed us. I was quite convinced that I never would anyway but I was still at the 'couldn't care less' stage and was, I believe, secretly admired by all the others for my nonchalant attitude. I think, in a way, I rather hoped they would throw me out as totally useless. Yet, on the other hand, my pride was unwilling to admit defeat so I found myself pondering over the intricacies of the liver and kidneys, the convolutions of the large intestine, the secrets of the middle ear, the blood stream and other mysteries of human organs by torchlight long after the ten o'clock lights out.

But on the Saturday morning while I was changing into a

clean apron following the housework session – we seemed to spend most of our time changing our aprons – I heard the gentle click of my neighbour's door. When I left my room she was just ahead of me along the corridor and I recognised the small slim girl with short dark hair whom I had noticed walking alone in the garden in the early morning, as I looked out of the window while cleaning my teeth. She appeared to be about my age – older than most of the others who were nineteen or twenty – and, like me, to be very much alone.

As we assembled in the practical room where we were introduced to Mrs. MacIntyre, I found myself standing next to her.

Mrs. MacIntyre was certainly a relief from bones, muscles, sinews and nerves and seemed to be a good- tempered old body quite willing to be pricked and bandaged and generally poked about by us all.

"Nurses," Nurse Thomas announced, holding Mrs. MacIntyre up by the scruff of her neck, her floppy legs dangling limply beneath the hem of her hospital nightgown, "you are to divide into twos and we are going to work with Mrs. MacIntyre."

She dumped our uncomplaining patient into a wheelchair and we all moved excitedly in the direction of the high pristine hospital bed towards which Mrs. M. was now being enthusiastically wheeled by three bright-eyed student nurses all anxious, I mentally noted, to please the teacher.

At last we were getting down to the real thing, beds and patients, even if the patient was filled with sawdust, had a thatch of wool for hair and a painted fish face with a perpetual grin.

In the general upheaval of moving us all, plus the patient, from one side of the room to the other, I once again found myself standing beside my neighbour and in the natural selection of things we were paired off. We were to have the thrilling task of sitting Mrs. M. onto a bedpan and then, after a respectful lapse of time, to take her off and settle her back into bed again. She was evidently a very sick patient who needed careful handling and one nurse couldn't perform such a delicate operation alone.

Nurse Thomas pointed to a tall skinny girl with glasses perched on a hook nose and said:

"Come with your partner nurse and we'll demonstrate together how to lift the patient, and then the others can divide up and take their turn."

We were only a handful for this high-powered manoeuvre as the rest of the class had gone off to practise some other heady stuff like learning how to fix two wooden legs on another sawdust patient before heaving her into a wheelchair. This was a strictly female household, and even the dolls were make-believe women.

Morley-Watson, the girl with the hook nose, was obviously taking her selection by Nurse Thomas very seriously. I still hadn't got to the point where I could or even wanted to take it all seriously. I imagined it would be time enough when I got onto the wards in the hospital proper and dealt with real flesh and blood, not realising that my hopes of doing anything of worth in the hospital could only be based on what I'd achieved in the classroom. Mercifully, this was only the first week and I still had twelve to go in which to realise my mistake. But Morley-Watson was just the contrary, all concentration, her brow deeply furrowed and her thin lips pressed tightly together as she was shown just how to put Mrs. MacIntyre into a position from where she could comfortably perform her natural functions. As I stood and watched I could see her head, crowned with a Sister's cap, in the not too distant future.

"Very GOOD Nurse," said Nurse Thomas, beaming her approval.

Poor old Morley-Watson turned crimson with embarrassment.

"Now then nurses," our instructor went on, "I want you all to come up here in turn and show how well you've understood what I've just demonstrated, and then we'll pretend Mrs. MacIntyre is unconscious – as if she wasn't! – and I'll show you how to give her a blanket bath."

We were really getting to grips with things.

I held back slightly and let the couple in front, who seemed to be bursting with excitement at the idea of showing what they'd learned, go ahead and demonstrate.

And then it was our turn.

We went forward and began our act.

"That's right, nurse," Nurse Thomas said encouragingly as we stood respectfully one on either side of the tall iron bed. "Now, you two grasp hands underneath the patient to support her."

We stood at the ready, poised to plunge.

"Don't forget," she warned, "Mrs. MacIntyre is a VERY SICK PATIENT and must be moved as little as possible."

I glanced down at the stupid, flaccid life-sized doll. She looked pretty healthy to me with her highly painted cheeks and flat mongolian face. I bent my head and bit my lip to suppress a giggle and, as Nurse Thomas hovered expectantly in the background with that wretched bedpan, waiting for just the right moment to shove it between the sheets, I grasped my neighbour's hands under the flaccid body and gently raised the doll in the air.

As I did so I touched something hard and metallic and, for a moment, was taken back. My neighbour was wearing a ring!

On our first evening in between all the other 'don't's Madonna had also mentioned that no jewelry of any kind was to be worn, no signet rings, no engagement rings, nothing.

"If you don't want to leave your rings lying around in your room then hang them on a ribbon round your neck and tuck them inside your dress," she had said.

I don't think anyone was engaged but there were a few signet rings which had immediately disappeared from view. Yet here was this girl STILL wearing a ring.

I tightened my grasp as we lowered Mrs. M. onto the bedpan, just to make sure. But there was no mistaking it, there was definitely a ring on her finger. As we stepped back to admire our handiwork and waited for the signal to return to action stations I tried to see her hand but we had been told that when we were standing still we ALWAYS had to have our hands locked behind our backs – and she had obviously taken this to heart. Seeing Nurse Thomas's eyes on me in disapproval I quickly shot mine into the required position, out of sight.

"NOW Nurses," Nurse Thomas continued once I had complied with the regulations, "I am going to remove the bedpan. Are you ready?"

We leapt to attention again.

As our hands shot forward to ease our patient into the air and gently lay her back on the pillows I looked hard at my companion's hand. She was wearing a slim gold band. A wedding ring!

My curiosity leapt to fever pitch. When we applied to train it had been made very clear to us that we were NOT allowed to be married and should we fall into the dreadful temptation of marrying while still in training, we would be asked to leave immediately.

"A nurse must be totally devoted to her work," I had been warned. "It is not possible to have divided loyalties."

That is why we were not, in those far off days, allowed to live out either. We all had to huddle cloistered together in hospital quarters in untainted celibacy.

How times have changed!

I could hardly wait for the lunch bell to ring and when it did I fell into step beside my partner and contrived to sit next to her at the table.

She smiled vaguely at me as we sat down but did not seem inclined to talk.

"I'm Baxter," I said, as the good wholesome food was passed along, volunteering information about myself for the first time since I'd arrived.

She looked up briefly.

"How do you do," she answered pleasantly. "I'm Warren-Smith."

And there the conversation ended.

But when the spotted dick pudding with the rather thin custard dribbling over it was placed before us I was beginning to get desperate, knowing that she could easily slip away and I wouldn't know the answer to the question which was now burning inside me.

"Are you enjoying the training?" I enquired.

She smiled but did not reply.

"It's jolly hard work," I went on, "harder than I thought it would be."

"Not a bad thing," she answered. "Keeps one from thinking."

And she pushed the plate with her pudding almost untouched away from her.

"I say," a rather plain, mousey girl sitting opposite breathed, leaning forward eagerly, her short-sighted eyes gleaming expectantly behind her thick horn-rimmed spectacles. "Aren't you going to eat it?"

My neighbour shook her head.

"Mind if I take it?" she asked breathlessly, her arm already stretched out, hovering in anticipation.

"Do," Warren-Smith replied, and pushed the plate into her eager hands.

The girl piled the spotted dick onto her empty plate and set to with gusto while those around who hadn't got the question in quickly enough looked on with envy. All that is except Morley-Watson.

Instantly her long nose protruded from a few places down the table, absolutely twitching with indignation.

"I say Davenport," she barked, her face an angry puce, "that's the THIRD time you've had Warren-Smith's pud this week."

Davenport looked up guiltily, her spoon wavering uncertainly in front of her wide open mouth.

I smiled across at her, not because I was in any way on her side but because her name brought back memories. My grandmother had always called a sofa a davenport, and as she sat there she looked like a sofa, squat, solid and comfortable. I thought how well her name suited her.

But she mistook my smile for encouragement and, without further ado, shoved the heaped-up spoon into her waiting mouth.

Morley-Watson obviously decided to admit temporary defeat. She withdrew her nose adding as an acid parting shot:

"Share and share alike you know!"

So that was it: I smiled to myself.

But the bell rang and we all leapt to our feet as Davenport shovelled up the last lumps of spotted dick.

"I'm going to see if there's any post," I volunteered to my neighbour. "Would you like me to look for you?"

"Thank you, but I'm not expecting anything," she said and glided into the crowd and out of sight.

Neither was I, it was just a conversational gambit, but now that I'd announced my intentions I felt obliged to go along to the front hall where the mail was laid out on a large table in alphabetical order.

Most people had already collected their letters and there were very few left. There was nothing for me but, out of curiosity, I looked in the W's. There WAS a letter for her, an envelope bearing an Admiralty crest. On an impulse I picked it up and, running up the stairs with it in my hand, knocked on her door.

She opened it and looked at me in surprise.

"There was nothing for me," I said, not quite knowing how she was going to take this intrusion. "But... I noticed this one for you."

She took it from me without a word and looked at the envelope.

As she did so her eyes filled with tears.

I stood there, not knowing what to say.

"Is there anything I can do?" I asked awkwardly. "Can I help?"

She shook her head slowly.

"Look," I said desperately, not only out of curiosity. My heart went out to her for whatever pain or tragedy she might be hiding as, for the first time since I arrived, I stopped thinking of myself. "I don't want to intrude or force anything on you but, well, we two are a little different from the others – we're older, we're not just out of school: perhaps we could get together, try to make all this bearable."

She smiled.

"You're right," she said, "it IS pretty unbearable."

"Did you realise it was going to be like this?" I asked.

She held open the door and I went in. As she flopped down on the bed, the letter still unopened in her hands, I sat on the hard wooden chair in front of the desk.

"I knew it wasn't going to be much fun," she said slowly.

"Then why did you come?"

She looked up at me and her eyes were a deep violet blue.

"I didn't know what else to do," she said quietly.

A silence fell between us which I couldn't see how to break without appearing indiscreet, or just plain downright rude.

She turned the envelope over in her hand but still didn't open it, and the pause between us lengthened unbearably.

"My husband went down on the Taurus," she said without looking up. "That's why I'm here. I had to do something and everything else I tried gave me too much time to think."

I bit my lip, not knowing what to reply, and I suddenly felt ashamed – ashamed of my self-pity and my selfishness. I wondered just what other hidden incentives there had been in the hearts and minds of the girls who had arrived to train at the same time as us, only one week before. Possibly none, I thought, they were all so young, hardly out of school: the war couldn't have touched them in the way it had touched her and me.

"I'm sorry," I said. There didn't seem to be much else to say.

To lose one's husband in wartime was a terrible thing but somehow, caught up in the misery and death all around, one had not had time to think. But the Taurus had been a peacetime disaster, a submarine which had set off on a routine training operation and never returned, with the loss of all on board. A peacetime disaster was somehow so much more difficult to cope with than a wartime one. It was so unexpected, so unnecessary.

"I'm South African," she said, breaking the silence, "from Cape Town."

I looked up in surprise; her accent had certainly not

given me any clue.

"I came over to join the F.A.N.Y.'S. Roddy and I met during the war and we were married just before D-Day. We weren't together a great deal but the Christmas before he went down we had bought a little cottage near Devonport: that was his base, and it seemed as if we were really going to begin our married life at last. We had so many plans for the future, not least the family we wanted to start."

She bit her lip.

"I found out a few days after he left that I was expecting a baby."

I felt a lump rise in my throat and swallowed quickly.

"Roddy never knew. It was a wonderful secret I was going to share with him as soon as he returned."

She looked up, and to my immense relief her deep blue eyes were dry. Had she broken down I know that my tears would have flowed with hers and I didn't want to upset the see-saw on which I was so precariously perched.

But as I looked across at her I saw a terrible bleak pain in their depths and the tightening of the muscles at the corner of her mouth, the slight frown between her brows, betrayed the extent of her unhappiness.

"But he never did," she said slowly, gazing intently at the ground as her foot described a series of circles on the bedside mat in front of her. "None of them did."

She paused and bit her lip.

"It was AWFUL," she burst out suddenly. "AWFUL. So many fine young men, our friends. Friends who had been with Roddy at Dartmouth at the outbreak of war, who had gone through those terrible convoys and survived."

There was a break in her voice but she swallowed hard and continued, her voice hardly above a whisper.

"And then to be swept away like that in PEACETIME."

Her quiet tone had developed a cutting edge and I felt frightened by her outburst. Frightened and vulnerable. I didn't want to get involved, and yet now there didn't seem to be any way out.

Oh why did I pick up that wretched letter, I thought desperately. Why didn't I mind my own business? I can't

Roddy Never Knew/ 43

cope with my own tangle of emotions at the moment, let alone take on someone else's.

My impulse was to get up, excuse myself and go, but my feet seemed to be riveted to the floor and I couldn't move. From a long way off I heard my voice say, "And the baby?"

"I lost it," she said. "Three weeks after I heard the news. THAT was the last straw."

And once again that tense silence fell between us. My feet still refused to budge, so I searched around desperately to change the subject.

"Couldn't you have gone home?" I enquired. "Back to South Africa?"

"I intended to, I've really very little to keep me here. Roddy's father was a rubber planter in Malaya, interned in Changi during the war. His mother was evacuated when the Japanese invaded but unfortunately she was on one of the ships which were torpedoed. Roddy's elder brother was killed in the Western Desert so, all told, it's a pretty tragic family. There's only his grandmother left here and she lives in the north of Scotland and is quite old. My father-in-law is still in Malaya. I've never met him though Roddy and I hoped to go out there to visit him once transport became easier, but I don't think he'll come back now after all these years: there's no longer anyone left for him to come back to."

She looked up with a sad smile.

"Getting a passage to the Cape is almost impossible for civilians at the moment; unless one is top priority there's not a hope for years."

She paused and sighed.

"I may go back later, I don't know. My mother would like me to, but would I settle after so long? It's a very different life. But anyway, in the meantime, I had to find something to do which would take my mind off what had happened. My friends tried to persuade me to stay in Devonport, but I couldn't."

Her voice broke but she recovered her composure and continued.

"I just couldn't. The Navy was everywhere and there were

too many reminders."

I nodded my head in sympathy and she looked across at me and smiled.

"Nursing seemed to be the answer. I'm fed, lodged and my nose will be kept to the grindstone all my working hours for the next four years. After that, I'll think again."

Her voice broke once more.

"Surely by then," she whispered, "the pain will have eased off."

She looked up at me pleadingly, as if I had the solution to her problem, and I trotted out the old platitude about time being the great healer: it was the only thing I could think of at that moment.

"If only the baby had lived," she mused, "I'd have had something to live for too."

She paused and a strange smile played round her lips.

"By some ironic twist of fate he would have been born last Saturday, the day I arrived here."

Everything was beginning to fall into place and I now understood that terrible heart-rending sobbing which I had heard coming from the other side of the wall on our first night here. My heart contracted. She had been crying not only for the young husband she had lost, but for the child she had never held in her arms. I felt the web of emotion tightening round me and as I struggled to free myself from its tangles I laughed: rather too loudly, once again afraid, trying to be flippant, trying to escape.

"How do you know it would have been a he?"

She smiled.

"I just know," she replied softly.

Then abruptly her tone changed. Perhaps she suddenly realised that she had revealed herself in an unguarded moment, opened up the raw bleeding depths, the secret agony in her life, and regretted it.

"Are you doing anything this afternoon?" she enquired.

"Not really," I answered, a little taken aback by her sudden change of tone. "I had thought of walking into town, what town there is, and trying to find a dry cleaners. I must have spilled tea on my skirt the day we arrived; there's a nasty stain right down the front and sponging hasn't done the trick."

"Do you mind if I come with you?"

"No, not at all. I'd be pleased to have your company," I heard myself saying and, strangely enough, I meant it. "It's our free afternoon, we might perhaps find Ye Olde Tea Shoppe and stuff ourselves with cream buns."

"I seem to have done nothing but stuff myself with starch since we arrived," she laughed. "If this stodge diet continues I'll WADDLE into the hospital when we finally get there."

And we both laughed, the tension broken, the link established.

"I'll just go and change," I said, getting up. "See you in fifteen minutes, down in the hall."

"Done," she replied, jumping off the bed.

But I stopped in the doorway, hesitant, not knowing quite what to say and yet urged to say something, to have everything clear between us. She turned from the wardrobe from which she had just taken down a soft grey woollen dress, and I closed the door and stood with my back to it.

"How PRETTY," I breathed, gazing at the dress in her hand.

"My mother sent it from South Africa," she said, giving it a shake.

"Might have guessed," I smiled, "I haven't seen anything so glamorous here for a long time."

She looked at me enquiringly, realising that it wasn't just to admire her dress that I had hesitated in the doorway, and I knew that if I didn't say then what was on my heart there would be a veil between us: suddenly, I wanted everything to be transparent.

"I've wanted to meet you all week," I said hesitantly.

She smiled encouragingly.

"I heard you crying on that first night and I knew then that there was something terribly wrong," I began and then the words seemed to dry up in my throat.

She bit her lip and put the dress, which she was still holding in her hand, down on the bed.

"I'm sorry I disturbed you," she said without looking up.

"Oh, it's not that," I hastened to add.

"No," she looked up and smiled, "I know it isn't."

She ran her hands thoughtfully across the soft grey folds.

"That first night not only did Roddy's death really hit me, perhaps because I'd finally made the break with everything which held me to him, but I couldn't help thinking about the baby and how different that day might have been."

She paused as if seeking the right words.

"I knew when I got into bed that a page had definitely turned: my life with Roddy and everything we'd hoped for had gone forever. A new phase was about to begin and it was a terrible awakening."

I leaned back against the door and looked at her. She appeared so frail and defenceless and young in the plain striped dress, like a prisoner in regulation garments, and my heart went out to her.

"Up until last Saturday I'd been busy. Life had gone on and I'd had my friends. Then suddenly I was alone and there was nothing but a great aching void."

"I know how you felt," I said quietly. "I felt like that too. But you still have your friends."

"It's not the same now," she went on. "They have their lives to live, lives all tied up with Devonport and the Navy. That's over for me. Even before I sold the cottage I knew I didn't belong any more: it was as if they were going one way and I was at a crossroads, not knowing which road to take. At least coming here has made it easier in a way: I've turned the corner and I've chosen a road. Whether it's the right road remains to be seen, only time will tell: but at least I'm not hovering with my future unknown. The days are mapped out for me and I don't have time to think."

I nodded and wondered if she was seeking the answer to that question which had been bothering me.

She smiled.

"I don't think you'll be kept awake again," she said.

I started to protest, but she broke in.

"No, honestly, I think that night really was the turning point: I'd stopped hovering and the decision had finally been taken – for better or for worse."

She grimaced.

"Seem to have heard that somewhere before."

For a moment there was a silence between us, but it was a comfortable silence, almost the silence of old friends.

"I may be alone here, " she ended, "but not as alone as I'd be on a busy naval base.

"I felt terribly alone last week too," I said slowly. "But I think it will be better now."

I hesitated, my hand on the doorknob.

"Perhaps we feel the same way about other things," I ventured.

She looked up.

"Such as...?"

"Well, this regimentation," I went on hesitantly, "this calling each other 'nurse' or by our surnames."

I paused and she smiled.

"I hate it too," she said. "At least when we're not in uniform let's drop it. I'm Jane."

I breathed a sigh of relief as more thawing began to take place inside me. So I wasn't being difficult, uncooperative, after all. Other women also felt as I did.

"I'm Noreen," I said and, without realising that the training was already beginning to bear fruit, turned and closed the door noiselessly behind me.

CHAPTER FIVE

That Nagging Question

The town, which I'd had no more than a glimpse of through the rain-spattered taxi window the day I arrived, proved to have more to it than I expected. After we had exhausted the thrills of Boots and Woolworths, we wandered along to the end of the main street where a dangling sign with *Elizabeth's* written in flowing script was creaking outside Ye Olde Tea Shoppe which we'd been sure we'd discover.

It was certainly old and as we peered through the bottled glass front door into the dark lamplit interior I saw hordes of student nurses sitting laughing and chatting at the polished oak tables scattered around the low beamed room.

Instinctively, I turned away: the last thing I wanted was a repetition of tea time up at the Old Lodge. But I was too late. Johnson stood up and waved to us.

"Come and join us," she called.

Jane and I looked at each other in dismay. I think the idea in both of our minds had been to escape, not to be swallowed up, but Johnson was such a warm, outgoing person it was difficult to refuse. I noted gratefully that Morley-Watson was sitting with what looked like another set of hockey players at a table in the far corner, so we would at least be spared that.

As I pushed open the door and we went in, one of the girls sitting with Johnson pulled round two chairs from an unoccupied table behind. Morley-Watson looked up disapprovingly at all this unauthorised reorganisation. She would, I thought, and had an insane desire to poke my tongue out at her.

Whatever's happening to you, I panicked, biting my lower lip in order to prevent my tongue from taking on a life of its own. Are you regressing to childhood or what?

The last time I'd poked my tongue out at anyone must have been all of twenty years before and I'd had my mouth washed out with soap and water as a punishment for being so impolite. I looked up, almost expecting the young waitress hovering over us in the frilly cap and apron to be holding the dreaded soap-filled sponge in her hand. But all she was wielding was a stubby pencil poised over her notepad.

As we gave our order I looked around and noticed most of my fellow students tucking into poached eggs or baked beans on toast.

"Is that all you're going to have?" Johnson enquired incredulously, as the waitress tripped away. "Don't you want...?"

I knew what she was going to say and I interrupted her before she could get it out.

"No thank you," I smiled. "Tea and scones will be just right for me."

I glanced across at Jane.

"Perhaps you...?"

"Oh no," she laughed. "It's the tea I want more than anything."

The others looked at us in amazement: we were actually refusing food.

These were the lean years after the war ended when rationing was still very much in force and any little extra one could scrounge was always gratefully stuffed into one's mouth.

I looked across the table at a beautiful willowy girl I had noticed during the week. She stood out because she seemed to be a particular friend of Johnson's and they made a rather Laurel and Hardy couple, Johnson short, fair, plump and always smiling and her companion tall, dark and serious with a dreamy, far-away look in her eyes.

"Were you two at school together?" I enquired.

"No," Johnson replied. "We met at the Guildhall."

"The Guildhall?" I queried, not understanding.

"Guildhall School of Music and Drama," Johnson replied. "Had to fill in a year after I left school before I could start training so I went to the Guildhall and it was there I met Rachel."

Rachel. What a beautiful name, and how it suited her delicate, classical beauty. It crossed my mind what a tragedy it would have been had Braithwaite been christened Rachel instead of Agnes, but then the thought that perhaps one becomes like one's name occurred to me and I started wondering what image Noreen conjured up in people's minds.

"What were you studying?" I turned to Rachel.

"The 'cello," she said dreamily.

"How lovely," I replied. "But why didn't you continue?"

"Oh, I'm not a professional," she laughed. "Never would be, but I enjoy playing and like Bunty, I had to fill in a year."

She paused.

"It was great fun, wasn't it Bunty?"

I looked in surprise from one to the other.

"Is Bunty REALLY your name?" I enquired.

Johnson looked at us mischievously then closed her eyes.

"No," she simpered, "it's...MARIgold!" and she fluttered her blonde eyelashes in a provocative fashion, placing her hands demurely together beneath her chin. Then, looking up, she burst out laughing.

"But I ask you. Do I LOOK like a MARIgold?"

And seeing her, we all burst into helpless giggles.

"I'm afraid I've never given much thought as to what a Marigold should look like," I said, wiping my eyes as I recovered.

"Well, certainly not like ME," Johnson replied and went off into further peals of laughter, which again brought a disapproving look from Morley-Watson.

"But why didn't you two sit together the first day?" I enquired, puzzled that Bunty should have had to recruit me to share her desk.

"Oh, Bunty's always late for EVERYTHING," Rachel said affectionately. "I was saving her a place next to me but someone came and asked if she could sit there, and I didn't like to say no."

"If you want we can change," I ventured.

Bunty rolled her eyes to the ceiling in mock horror.

"CHANGE!" she echoed dramatically. "Long Annie would have a fit."

"Long Annie?" I queried, and then realised that that was their name for the Sister I had nicknamed Madonna.

There were more giggles all round.

"Anyway," Rachel continued, "we share a room. We don't need to be glued together like Siamese twins." .

This was news to me. I had imagined that everyone had little individual cells like Jane and me, and mentioned the fact.

"Oh no," Bunty replied, "there are four of us in our room."

"Four," I exclaimed, "how ghastly."

"It wouldn't be," she sniffed, "except that one is Morley-Watson, and she's a pain in the neck."

We all laughed. I could well imagine.

"Only because you're so hopelessly untidy," Rachel grinned, "and she isn't. If you'd pick up all the things you drop just once in a while life would be easier for all of us."

I could picture the scenario.

"She sets her alarm for SIX," Bunty hissed, "so that she can chew over all those old bones and guts we're supposed to have memorised."

I looked from one to the other. I couldn't imagine anything more appalling than being obliged to share a room with Morley-Watson.

"We have our own rooms," I said.

"In deference to your great age," Bunty replied in mock solemnity, and we all burst out laughing again.

It was a long time since I had laughed in such a carefree fashion, and I began to feel a warmth towards these girls who had become part of my life.

"We thought you were terribly toffee-nosed when you arrived," Bunty went on. "But you're really quite human."

"Oh BUNTY," Rachel groaned. "Why do you ALWAYS put your foot in it?"

I smiled reassuringly and winked at Bunty.

"What were you studying at the Guildhall?" I asked her.

"Singing," she smiled and, her china blue eyes twinkling more than ever, she opened her mouth.

"Bunty, NO," Rachel said sharply.

"If you don't watch her," she smiled, turning to me, "she is capable of bursting into *Tosca* without warning."

As our tea arrived, Bunty collapsed into more giggles.

"Nice to know that you all have other names besides Nurse," Jane said to the table at large as I handed her a cup. "Noreen and I have decided when we're out of uniform to drop the formalities. I'm Jane."

We all exchanged names and then settled down to the serious business of eating and, as a pleasant silence hovered cosily over our little table, I felt the thawing process inside me continue: the tip of the iceberg had been touched when Johnson had offered to share her desk with me and I felt now that perhaps the huge mountain which had been lodged underneath was gradually melting away.

I looked around the table at the faces of my four companions, three of them not long out of school, whose lives I had pledged to share for the next four years and, for the first time in a week, I didn't groan inwardly at the thought. The dull dark cloud which had hung menacingly over my future seemed to be gradually evaporating to show the sun struggling to break through, and as we munched together in contented silence, for the first time since I arrived, I had a semblance of peace. I stopped striving for identity, stopped drawing in my antennae, stopped sitting precariously at the top end of the see-saw dreading to be let down but, slowly, let it drop into position until my feet touched the ground. And as they did so, and I mentally saw myself get off and walk away, I knew there was a reason why I was here.

I hadn't got all the answers to the questions I'd been asking myself. In fact, I hadn't got any of the answers, but at least they were not dogging my every waking moment. I wasn't perpetually asking myself, 'What's the point?' At that moment in time I was content just to carry on, convinced that one day I *would* find those answers. I knew, deep inside me, that I was on the right path, the path which would lead me to the solution, where those nagging questions would disappear.

As I sat in the cosy low-ceilinged room, with chintz curtains at the tiny latticed windows and matching cushions tied to the wheel-backed chairs, warmed by the gentle hum of conversation which had started up again at our table, my mind went back to the previous summer, just after I had made my decision and been accepted for training. I had been holidaying on the Baltic sea-coast with some Swedish friends and I remembered very clearly a conversation we had had one evening on the terrace of their summer house, gazing dreamily out over the incredibly clear waters as we watched the northern sun dip lower and lower into the sea but never actually disappear. I had gone there hoping that a change from London would inject me with new life and fresh hope, giving me a reason for living and supplying the solution to all my problems. But once there, I had realised that I had merely shifted my questions to another location. I still hadn't found any answers, and my Swedish friends didn't have any either.

"You're the one who should have all the answers to life," they had laughed, during one of our evening philosophical discussions. "England is a God-fearing country where people go to church and believe in something."

I had agreed. But it wasn't as easy as they imagined.

I had been taken to church from an early age but, although it was a pleasant weekly ritual, it hadn't given me the truth I was seeking, and continued to seek subconsciously even while riding the post-war merry-go-round.

"In Sweden, we worship the welfare state," they'd said.

"Don't people go to church at all here?" I'd enquired.

"Not many. There was a religious community in the south some years ago. An order of nuns," one answered reflectively, "but they've gone. Most of us believe that man is his own master, free to do as he wishes, and it seems to work. We don't need religion, we have equality, prosperity and everything we want without it."

On the surface it appeared to be true. In the late forties

Sweden was a land flowing with milk and honey, so different from England where we were still strictly rationed for everything, often cold because of the fuel shortage, and where the post-war slogan of promised prosperity and a better life for all didn't so far seem to have got off the ground.

I had been tempted by my friends' theories and began to wonder if perhaps they weren't right after all. They hadn't said I was crazy to want to train as a nurse but they had been practical, materialistic, told me to make sure that my working hours would be congenial and that I was going to be paid well for what I did.

All these thoughts went through my mind as I sipped my tea and I smiled to myself, realising that here I was, doing the exact opposite to all my Swedish friends had advised. My salary during training was to be the princely sum of five pounds a month and, if this last week's action programme was anything to go by, I would have to work all hours and no redress.

I could almost hear the laughter on the other side of the North Sea.

"Hey Baxter, what are you grinning about?" Bunty's voice broke in on my dreaming. "Stop waving your cup around in the air and come back to earth."

Her foot kicked me sharply under the table and I realised that I was sitting gazing into space, my cup suspended in front of me. I looked at her laughing face and smiled.

"Where were you?" she grinned.

I grinned back but didn't reply. Suddenly, as if a light had been switched off inside her, the grin faded and those mischievous china blue eyes widened and became even larger as they riveted on the door.

Its bell tinkled as four young men in clerical collars came in and sat down at a table near the window.

Bunty's eyes shot heavenwards in a voluptuous gesture.

"Curates," she breathed ecstatically.

I looked across in amusement at Rachel, who merely shrugged her shoulders.

"Don't take any notice of her," she said matter-of-factly,

"she's got a THING about curates."

And turning to her friend she pulled her arm sharply.

"Bunty stop it," she hissed. "You're STARING."

"Wouldn't you?" Bunty drooled, swivelling her gaze round to us. "FOUR of them, all at once."

"You're HOPELESS," Rachel laughed.

"There must be a theological college somewhere around here," I mused. "No town would have FOUR curates."

"Oh, the bliss," Bunty sighed. "I'm coming here every Saturday afternoon... just to GAZE."

And she turned her head dreamily in the direction of the table under the window where the four young men were intently studying the menu.

"Oh shut up, you ass," Rachel laughed, grabbing her friend's head and turning it forcibly back in our direction. "Have another poached egg instead."

The waitress seemed to know the young clerics and was chatting amicably with them while taking their orders. As she turned to leave Bunty beckoned to her.

"Where do THEY come from?" she whispered darkly, nodding her head towards the curates.

"From the seminary in the next town," the waitress replied. "They often come in here for tea."

Bunty's mouth dropped open.

"The SEMINARY," she wailed. "You mean they're Roman CATHOLICS?"

"Yes," the waitress smiled, "studying to be priests."

As she left, a suppressed giggle went round the table at Bunty's woebegone expression.

"Oh the pathos," she moaned dramatically. "The utter pathos."

Then she joined in the laughter. It was difficult to suppress her bouncing joie de vivre for long.

On leaving the tea shop she gazed longingly at the table where the four young men were deep in conversation.

"Just my luck," she repeated, shaking her head sadly, as the door closed behind us.

We wandered together back through the town and up the hill. I found myself walking with the fifth person at the table, a girl whom I hadn't even noticed as part of the intake until we entered the tea shop. And then the conversation had been so dominated by Bunty's sense of fun and backchat that she hadn't had much chance to join in.

"Bunty and I were at school together," she said as we strolled along. "She hasn't changed."

And she smiled.

"Are you in the same room as she and Rachel?" I enquired.

"No," she said. "I'm on the top floor."

"Alone?" I asked.

"Oh no, there are four of us," she replied.

I grimaced.

"Four seems to be the magic number."

"There are six in some rooms," she went on.

"Don't you MIND?" I asked.

She shrugged.

"It's not much different from being at school," she smiled. "I went to Switzerland for a year to fill in time before coming here and there we were ten to a room so, in a way, this is an improvement."

I realised then just how wide the gap was between Jane and me and the rest of the intake. How remote they were even from the war, which had played such an important and devastating part in both our lives. How much the six years since I had left school and been immediately plunged into one of the most terrible holocausts the world had ever known had changed me.

And I looked across at Pamela, striding purposefully at my side, and understood that we came from two different worlds.

"So all this isn't so bad for you?" I enquired.

She looked at me in surprise.

"All what?" she replied.

"Oh, I don't know," I shrugged. "All this rushing to answer bells, being treated as half-wits, being regimented..."

Her eyes widened in surprise.

"No," she answered. "Why should it be?"

"No reason," I said as we turned into the wide tree-lined

drive. "I suppose I'm just out of the habit. Or," I paused and smiled, "perhaps it's just my great age."

And we both laughed.

CHAPTER SIX

Is He Going to Live?

If the previous Saturday, the day we had all arrived at the Preliminary Training School, had marked a turning point in life for Jane, the following Saturday certainly marked a turning point for me. It was the day when I finally relaxed, stopped asking questions to which there was not then any immediate answer, turned my back on all that had gone before and decided that I was in this new life, by my own choice as Jane had remarked, for better or for worse, and that I would make the best of it whatever happened.

And as I settled down to this reality a new pattern began to form. The people I met and mingled with every day, the girls with whom I shared not only the menial domestic tasks and the practical schoolroom work but every waking hour, subtly changed and became human beings with recognisable faces, real people whom I wanted to get to know, not just featureless statues to be avoided at all costs. Everything took on another aspect and although I cannot say that I enjoyed every minute of every day, I found myself laughing more spontaneously and more often that I had done for some time, as we all joined together and took the rough with the smooth. And in those far off days there was certainly a lot of rough attached to a nurse's training.

All too soon the end of our initial three months crept up on us and the dreaded yet longed-for day when we would finally be 'on the wards' and dealing with real people and not stuffed dolls and theories began to loom menacingly, and yet tantalisingly, ahead.

We all knew that the time was coming when our sheltered, if frustrating, life would be over and we would really be in action, coming to grips with the stark realities of life and death. As that day drew nearer, we were taken for one half day a week to the main hospital to taste what 'being on the wards' was really like.

Our departure for London by coach on that first morning resembled a cross between the gathering of the guests for a garden party at Buckingham Palace and a Sunday school outing as we crackled, stiff with starch, all spit and polish and shiny noses, into the waiting coach, anxious to present our best faces to the ward to which we had been assigned. The atmosphere inside the coach was electric with our suppressed excitement and near hysterical giggles, which spattered forth as it bowled along the now leafy lanes in the bright morning sunshine and manoeuvred through the grimy backstreets of London, finally stopping in front of the old hospital's great entrance door.

I don't think there was a heart which was not beating at double the normal rate as we were herded off by Nurse Thomas and directed to the wards which, once we finally went to the hospital to work full time, would be our bases for the next three months.

I was assigned to a men's surgical ward on the top floor.

It was a warm late spring day and when I arrived diffidently at the door of the long ward I realised just what the last three months of indoctrination had done to me. The once poised, confident young woman who had never batted an eyelid at going anywhere now stood trembling on the threshold, dreading admission.

The sight of two rows of beds neatly aligned on the polished floor, the unlit leaded stove at the far end around which a group of men in dressing gowns were reading newspapers or idly chatting and the brisk crackle of starched aprons as nurses, perhaps only a few months senior to me but at that moment divided from me in experience by light years, bustled confidently backwards and forwards, completely ignoring me, sapped my already vastly depleted confidence and reduced me to a state of near panic.

"Don't just stand there nurse," one of them said. "Come in. You're here for the afternoon I suppose?"

I nodded dumbly.

She looked at me in a superior fashion. I later discovered

that she was from the intake above me, only three months my senior, but obviously anxious to throw off on to someone new all the injuries she had suffered during her own initiation. But at the time, if she had been God she couldn't have inspired greater awe in me.

I stumbled after her into the ward.

"Leave your cloak in the linenry," she said exasperatedly. "You don't think you're going to wear it in HERE, do you?"

I shook my head, and wondered where the linenry was.

She pointed imperiously in its direction and I obediently went and hung up my cloak with all the others, then braced myself for whatever horror might be in store.

As I went back into the ward, a middle-aged man in the first bed looked up from his magazine and winked.

I half smiled in return and my spirits rose. I felt I had found a friend.

Another nurse, whose vintage I couldn't even guess at, now bustled to my side.

"You from the P.T.S.?" she enquired.

I nodded, all power of speech seemingly having left me.

"What's your name?"

"Baxter," I managed to whisper.

"Well Baxter," she said, "go to the sluice."

She stopped and motioned to the girl who had been so bossy when I first arrived.

"Meredith," she said. "Take Baxter to the sluice and show her where everything is. There's a lot of dirty linen from this morning: the two of you had better get it ready for the laundry."

Meredith didn't even bother to look in my direction. She just marched off to the other end of the ward and I meekly followed.

As we entered the sluice a strangely pungent smell hit me. It was a smell I was to recognise throughout my training and almost come to ignore, the permeating sweet-sour odour of soiled linen and fresh blood combined. Meredith handed me the inevitable long-handled scrubbing brush, took one herself, turned on the cold water tap in the high, wide sluice basin and indicated an enormous pile of freshly stained sheets heaped on the floor.

Once out of the ward she became slightly more human, but not much;

"Better get going," she sighed. "There'll be more to come, we had ten go down to the theatre this morning."

And together we approached the pile and selected our share.

Not daring to begin the conversation I waited for Meredith to open up, but she didn't seem inclined to.

"Will we be doing this all afternoon?" I enquired at last.

"You must be joking," she replied scathingly. "All this lot had better be out of the way before Sister arrives at two, or else there'll be ructions."

We doggedly scrubbed for a few minutes in silence.

"Is she a dragon?" I ventured at last.

"Worse," Meredith replied laconically. "Dragons don't snort fire ALL the time."

And there all conversation ended. But it had given me an insight, shown me why Meredith was as she was. And I vaguely wondered whether in three months' time when the next unfortunate intake came up for their afternoon on the wards I would have stopped trembling and become like her.

Just when my arms were beginning to feel as if they didn't belong to me any more and were about to fall off, a pretty young nurse with a mop of flaming red curls popped her head round the door of the sluice.

"Time to report," she hissed. "Sister's size ten boots have been heard tramping the corridor."

Meredith dropped her scrubbing brush as if it had suddenly become red hot and, turning off the cold running water, said to me, "Smooth out your apron, she hates creases. And now for it."

Quickly brushing down my apron and patting my butterfly cap into place I hurried after her out of the sluice and back into the almost silent ward. The men around the unlit stove were now slumbering or nodding over their newspapers and those in bed had either settled down for a snooze or were lying pensively, hands clasped behind their heads, gazing up at the stark white ceiling. Nothing stirred.

It was like the deathly hush before the storm, the terrible eerie silence which falls just before a tornado screeches down a deserted street.

I slipped into place beside Meredith, not knowing where else to go. All the nurses were standing to attention, hands behind their backs in front of the desk in the middle of the ward. No one appeared to be breathing. When I thought that the tension must surely explode, the door at the bottom of the ward swung open and the tallest woman I had ever seen walked in. She must have been over six feet, but with the high starched cap sitting stiffly on her head adding even more inches, she looked like Goliath in person.

To say she walked would have been a misnomer: she lolloped with a peculiar rolling gait not unlike that of a sailor when he first touches dry land after months at sea, her stiff white apron barely moving on her skeletal-like frame. As I watched her advance towards us, looking neither to right nor left, I remember thinking that I had never seen anything so narrow outside of a tube of toothpaste. She sat down at the desk and glanced at the notes arranged in a neat pile, before raising pale washed-out eyes to the group standing stiffly to attention in front of her.

I held my breath, but she did not appear even to notice that I was there. She didn't speak, merely raised her eyebrows and the senior nurse, (I recognised her as such because her dress had different coloured stripes from the rest of us) began to make her report on what had happened since Sister had left the ward at ten o'clock that morning.

Sister didn't look at anyone and she didn't appear to be listening, though every now and then the two hairs which protruded from a mole on her chin twitched. I was fascinated.

As the senior nurse finished she nodded and half of the group detached themselves and marched from the ward for their few hours off, leaving just four of us standing like ramrods in front of her.

"Nurse Montgomery," she said at last, and her voice sounded as if she were gargling with marbles, "go down to the basement theatre and bring back Mr. Evans. They've just telephoned to say he'll be ready to come up in five minutes. You can take the PTS with you," she added as an afterthought.

So she had noticed I was there.

"Nurse Meredith, you go to the linenry and make bandages and fold gauze squares. Nurse Spencer…"

I never found out what assignment Spencer had been given because Montgomery had twitched at my apron, jerking her head in the direction of the door, and I trotted obediently after her.

Montgomery was a bright young thing with a friendly smile, which was a relief. I could see from her white belt that she had passed her preliminary exams and was out of her first year, and felt confident that at least one of us knew what we were doing. We scurried down the stairs.

"Thank goodness we're collecting a patient," Montgomery laughed, "at least we can take the lift to come back. I've been dashing up and down Regent Street all morning trying to get the best value for my coupons: my sister's getting married next month and I HAVE to have a new dress, but it wasn't easy and my feet are killing me."

She stifled a laugh as we tripped down the last few stairs and began to walk primly, eyes cast down, along the crowded main hall. Nurses, doctors, medical students, physiotherapists, patients in wheelchairs, patients in dressing gowns, patients on their way to the different clinics, some looking purposeful, some completely bewildered by the immensity of it all, swirled round us as we walked its length then slipped down the last flight of stairs to the basement.

"We could have come straight down here," Montgomery confided as we went into the long lighted corridor, "it would have been quicker, but I think it's much more fun to walk along the upstairs hall where there's some life, rather than scramble about here in the gloom."

And this time she let her laughter peal out. There was no one to give a reproving frown. She seemed a jolly girl and my heart warmed for the first time that day to think that when I finally came to work on the wards in just two weeks' time, I would have at least one person who didn't take every second of life in deadly earnest.

The basement theatre we went to was a startling place. It had been set up as an emergency theatre during the war, and until the hospital's extensive bomb damage was repaired it would remain in operation. Montgomery took it all in her stride but I had never been hospitalised – not, that is, since I had my tonsils removed at the age of four, and I didn't remember much about that. All this was very new to me: even frightening.

"Hallo Fred," Montgomery greeted the porter who was waiting in the theatre ante-room as we entered. "I've brought the PTS with me to get her acquainted with the horrors of the theatre."

And off she pealed again.

Fred nodded sympathetically in my direction.

"Don't take any notice of her, nurse," he said kindly. "Always one for a bit of a laugh."

I smiled.

"It's a nice change," I replied.

Just then the door opened and a theatre nurse, dressed from head to foot in green, came out wheeling a trolley on which a young man was lying. For a moment I thought he was dead. His face was devoid of any colour and he seemed quite lifeless, but no one else appeared to be in the least perturbed. The theatre nurse turned to Montgomery, handing her a file of notes and giving her instructions about a bottle of something which was attached to a pole at the head of the trolley and from which a colourless liquid was dripping down a tube into a vein in the patient's arm.

The porter opened the door and then pushed the trolley back into the lighted corridor, with Montgomery and me walking beside it rather like the mourners round an Indian funeral bier.

"Is he going to live?" I whispered to Montgomery as we trotted along beside the trolley.

She looked at me in amazement.

"LIVE!" she echoed and off she went again, almost doubled up with laughter.

I felt rather foolish.

"He's only had a HERNIA," she chortled. "Of course he'll live."

I coloured in confusion.

"It's nurse's first day," the porter said to her reproachfully. "You've forgotten what YOU felt like the first time you took a patient up from the theatre."

Montgomery stopped laughing immediately and blew me a kiss across the trolley.

"Sorry," she said apologetically. "It's amazing how quickly one gets used to things. I DO remember the first time. I almost had hysterics, and the patient had only had a broken nose fixed. By the time you've been on the ward a week you'll quickly be able to recognise the living from the dead."

And the twinkle in her eyes showed that she was threatening to go off into more gales of laughter. She reminded me of a slender Bunty.

"You are a one, nurse," the porter said, shaking his head in mock indignation.

It was quite obvious that Montgomery was indeed a One, and a very popular one with all the members of the staff who didn't happen to be actually in authority.

Waiting for the lift I looked down once again at the man lying grey and unconscious on the trolley beside me and I realised for the first time how ephemeral our life is down here, how taut the thin line which separates us from death. Standing there in that long deserted corridor a Bible passage I had learned by heart in Sunday school many years before came back to my mind: we are like a blade of grass, here today and gone tomorrow. And I shuddered as the words which had ceased haunting me during the last few weeks slipped back into my brain. Why am I here? What's life all about?

The lift jolted to a stop and we got out. As I looked at the still figure lying beside me something told me that in probing the depths, in learning about human suffering and pain, I would find the answer. And this assurance quietened my thoughts and gave me peace.

Once back in the ward the afternoon seemed to rush by.

Montgomery had been given to me as a guardian angel and I dogged her every footstep, grateful to have found someone who appeared to be human in this starched antiseptic atmosphere.

Just before five thirty the nurses who had had the afternoon off reported back on duty and as we all presented ourselves once again in front of Sister's desk she looked up, not at me but past me and said:

"The PTS nurse had better go now, or she'll miss the bus."

I didn't quite know how I was supposed to take my leave and for one crazy moment thought perhaps I ought to curtsey, but mercifully Montgomery kicked my foot and once again jerked her head imperceptibly in the direction of the door.

I glided out and almost ran down the stairs, until I remembered that a nurse must never, in any circumstances, even if it meant missing the bus back, hurry or appear flustered, so slowed my steps and set off purposefully along the main corridor, trying to look for all the world as if I'd been doing it for years, yet terrified in case any of the civilians wandering around looking bewildered should ask me for directions.

The bus was waiting at the main door, almost full. Jane waved to me from a seat near the back and I climbed in and sank gratefully down beside her.

"How was it?" she asked pleasantly.

I pursed my lips and sighed.

"You first," I replied grimly.

"Oh, it was lovely," she said, her eyes shining enthusiastically. "Sister's an absolute sweetie and was SO kind and helpful."

I thought I must be hearing wrongly.

"I've had a wonderful afternoon," she enthused. Sister took me under her wing and showed me the ropes herself."

I let out a low whistle.

"Lucky you," I said.

"Why, what was yours like?"

"Dante's inferno," I replied.

She laughed.

"Oh come on, it can't have been as bad as all that."

I smiled.

"Well, perhaps not QUITE as bad, but very nearly. The Sister I had didn't address one word to me. As far as she's concerned I don't think I existed or if I did it was just as a nuisance."

"Perhaps it'll be better when you're actually working there," Jane soothed.

"Perhaps," I answered grimly, "but I don't hold out much hope."

As the doors closed and the bus prepared to draw out into London's traffic I glanced curiously at Jane from under my lashes.

She was leaning back in her seat, her eyes far away, a contented smile on her lips.

Must be because she's been given such a plum, I thought enviously.

Then my eyes turned surreptitiously towards her again and I realised that that was certainly not the only reason. She had subtly changed in the few weeks since we had first met and there seemed to be a real peace, an aura of serenity surrounding her. The tenseness had gone from her body, the outline of her cheeks had softened and her eyes no longer held that look of a wounded fawn. And I vaguely wondered what had happened to her during the last three months to bring about such a transformation.

The buzz of animated conversation all around broke in on my musings and took my thoughts off Jane as I sleepily tuned into the excited schoolgirl chatter. It was liberally spattered with Sister this and Sister that – I didn't appear to be the only one who had not picked a winner judging from the groans which rose and fell – but gradually, as we left the dust and grime of London behind us and began to wind out into the evening sun setting over rural England, the voices died down as, one by one, our heads nodded forward and our eyes closed. The afternoon had been an excitement and a strain for us all and we were beginning to ask ourselves how we would ever stand up to the long hours and the hard daily grind when we finally achieved our goal and were on the wards.

By the time the bus finally turned into the drive of the Old Lodge and slid past the multicoloured blaze of rhododendrons, now in full bloom, its passengers were blissfully unaware of the sweet perfume of early roses which filled the soft evening air. We were all fast asleep.

CHAPTER SEVEN

A Yearning for Hope

The excitement and fatigue of that half day spent doing the real thing became a reality all too soon. My first morning as a junior probationer started at five forty-five when the electric bell once again crashed into my dreams.

The bus to take us from the nurses' home to the hospital would be leaving at six fifteen and not only did I have to be dressed and ready, my bed made and my room tidied, but I also had five flights of stairs to run down – all in not much more than twenty minutes.

Crawling sleepily out of bed on that lovely early summer morning I glanced through the window and caught a glimpse of the Thames flowing lazily by on the other side of the road.

I had been delighted the evening before to discover that I had been allocated this charming triangular-shaped corner room at the top of the building, with windows giving on to not only a view of the river but the whole sweep of the Thames and the bridges spanning its banks. Jane was no longer next door and had not been as fortunate as I. Her room was on the second floor and overlooked the courtyard, but she had Rachel and Bunty as neighbours.

When I ran quickly down the steep flight of stairs and into the hall, the first bus had already left and the second was just drawing away. The third and last, its engine running, was almost full. As I climbed in, Rachel appeared: I had heard her shouting to Bunty to hurry up when I was in the stair well.

"Please PLEASE could you wait," she pleaded. "My friend won't be a minute."

The driver looked at his watch.

"Only a minute then," he replied.

Rachel rushed back inside and came out a few seconds later dragging a bleary-eyed and rather dishevelled Bunty behind her. As she shoved her friend into the bus the driver accelerated and moved away.

"You're jolly lucky it's JOHN," a voice from the back I recognised as belonging to Meredith said disapprovingly. "SID wouldn't have waited."

Bunty looked round, obviously making a mental note never to travel with Sid but, as always, finding it difficult to take anything seriously. Attempting to fix her cap in a mirror which Rachel was holding up for her, she just grinned over her shoulder.

"You PTS lot had better learn that time is time," Meredith grunted in a parting shot as the bus bowled along the almost deserted Embankment in the peace and freshness of that sparkling June morning. "What a CHEEK, keeping us all waiting."

She sniffed indignantly and I half expected to hear an approving snort coming from Morley-Watson, then realised that she and her gang would almost certainly have been in the first bus to leave. They had probably been dancing on the pavement in excited anticipation of all the thrills the day had in store, long before it even left its depot.

Somehow we all got through that day with its stark reality after so much make-believe, its new faces, new experiences, new impressions – and the next day and the next, returning to our rooms in the evening limp and exhausted, our feet sore and often swollen, our minds and our bodies so weary that we were apt to fall asleep on our knees during evening prayers before the lights were dimmed in the ward.

Sister still didn't seem to notice that I was there, but at least I had a handle to my name now and was no longer referred to by her as the PTS. I tried to make myself inconspicuous, scurrying around behind Montgomery as much as I could and avoiding Meredith whenever possible.

Being one of the junior nurses, the lowest of the low, classed even below the cleaning staff, I had a great deal to do with the patients since we were given the most menial tasks: dusting bed frames, washing the tops of lockers and endlessly fetching and carrying the heavy wooden-framed green-curtained screens whenever a patient was washed, examined, given an injection or needed a bedpan. Although we were always given far more than I considered it humanly possible to get through in the allotted time and then were in trouble if we didn't finish early, we did all the same manage to chat to the patients as we swung about under the beds, seeing that the wheels were correctly positioned all facing inwards, that there was not one speck of dust or fluff in sight, and that everything on the locker was standing in place with military precision. And I soon realised how much more satisfying it was to deal with real people rather than with stuffed dolls. True, we had been able to pull poor old Mrs. M. around as much as we wanted and then just dump her anywhere when we'd finished, but if there had been no complaint, there hadn't been any response, any sign of recognition either.

Now I was face to face with the real thing, with human beings, with suffering humanity in all its forms, and as the days went by I appreciated the time I was able to spend with the patients. There were some who grumbled non-stop but mostly they were cheerful and uncomplaining and there were others who seemed to have a little extra something which set them apart, made them different, helped them to come to terms with whatever burden or pain they were experiencing and kept them at peace no matter what happened. And they intrigued me.

Sister, for some unknown reason, did not encourage us to talk to the patients, and one of the only times she addressed me directly in those early days was when she thought I had lingered longer than was necessary tidying the locker of the friendly policeman who had winked so conspiratorially at me on the first afternoon.

It had been a long hot tiring day, the first Saturday, and I was beginning to wonder whether I'd even make it till my day off on the Monday. We were getting ready for the ward's annual spring clean and everything, but EVERYTHING, had to be extra scrubbed and docketed methodically. Sister had been chivvying and nagging all afternoon and by the time the patients' evening meal was cleared away I was wilting. As I furiously dusted the bedside lockers for the umpteenth time that day I began thinking about the way most of my friends would have spent that glorious Saturday afternoon: on the river, picnicking, or even at a late point-to-point, and as a huge wave of shallowly buried self-pity washed over me, my eyes filled with tears.

My policeman friend must have sensed that I'd almost had enough.

"What's the matter nurse?" he said sympathetically. "The old girl been at you again?"

The odd thing was that Sister was not old. She could only have been in her mid-thirties, but to me she seemed like Methuselah, and maybe to him too.

I nodded dumbly, unable to speak. He leaned over, fished in his locker and brought out a bar of milk chocolate.

"Here," he whispered, "go into the sluice and enjoy this: it'll make you feel better."

With sweet rationing still strictly in force, a whole bar of chocolate was a treat indeed, and it must have been a sacrifice for him to offer it.

But Sister's eagle eyes had taken in the situation.

"Nurse," she gargled, lolloping over in my direction. "Take these porringers into the sluice and see that they are scrubbed PROPERLY. I don't know what you think you did with them this afternoon, they're a DISGRACE."

My mouth opened and shut and without a word I took the porringers and fled to the sluice.

Sister's head appeared after me in the doorway.

"And," she grated, "we do not accept presents from patients... ever."

She paused and breathed deeply, the whiskers on her chin twitching in indignation.

"Not even a bar of chocolate."

And she held out her hand.

I dug into my dress pocket and dropped the precious chocolate into it. As she disappeared, the rustle of her apron betraying her anger, I buried my face in the crumpled roller towel hanging limply on the wall and sobbed.

That night as I lay in wakeful misery, listening to the sound of singing coming from the decks of the pleasure steamers as they sailed back up the Thames towards Westminster Bridge, I honestly wondered whether I could carry on.

But what was the alternative?

I knew I couldn't go back. One never can, and if one tries it is usually a bitter disappointment. Already in the three months since I had withdrawn from my old circle of friends I felt that a distance had been created between us: we were not on the same wavelength any more, our lives were so totally opposed. Even without admitting it, I knew that my values had changed and we no longer laughed at the same things.

The revelry on the river died down and the dawn chorus broke softly, then rose in crescendo over sleeping London. I fell into a fitful sleep, only to be awakened by the screeching bell.

It was Sunday and, dragging my aching feet up the stairs to the ward, I wondered how I was going to face the sympathetic policeman whose generous gift had been unceremoniously returned to him the evening before. There was a strange lull over everything. The atmosphere was different; there was a more leisurely approach to our usually frantic early morning routine and the rhythm of the ward had subtly changed.

Once breakfast was over and the beds had been straightened and tidied yet again, instead of standing in front of Sister's desk like marble statues waiting to report, the nurses all gathered around the upright piano in the middle of the ward and, to my amazement, I was handed a pile of hymn books and told to give one to each patient. Sister was in her room at the end of the ward talking to the relatives of an elderly man who had died during the night and as Montgomery took her seat on the piano stool the Charge Nurse walked in and announced the first hymn. Montgomery broke into the opening chords of *Praise my Soul the King of Heaven* and most of the men sitting up in bed joined in heartily. Even those who were flat on their backs did their best to sing with a nurse or another patient holding the hymn book in position for them.

It was a short service but a beautiful one. As my eyes wandered round the spotless ward during the singing of the last hymn I noticed many a tear being surreptitiously brushed away from a damp cheek, and I realised that most of these men had been touched by its simplicity. Perhaps, I couldn't help wondering, there is something in religion after all, something more than the weekly churchgoing and nightly set prayer ritual which had always been my habit.

While we were collecting up the hymn books and the men settled down to read the Sunday papers, Sister came in and sent for me. After our encounter of the evening before I went over in fear and trembling, wondering what else I had done wrong.

"There are four patients who would like to go to the chapel for morning service: two will need wheelchairs and the other two can walk," she said without looking directly at me. "I'm sending you with Nurse Montgomery and Nurse Spencer to look after them. The service is at ten thirty so you'd better start getting them ready. Nurse Montgomery will tell you what to do."

And she turned away to check the drip of a young man who had been admitted the evening before.

While Spencer and I pushed the two wheelchairs out on to the landing, Montgomery followed with the walking wounded and, sheer bliss, we pressed the button and waited for the lift to take us down to the first floor. When we got out there were many other nurses milling about the corridor, some behind wheelchairs, some with patients leaning heavily on their arms and some off duty, all walking in the direction of the chapel, which was already more than half full when we entered its dim interior.

We had only just settled our patients onto the dark wooden pews when the chaplain entered and the service began. It was matins, a liturgy which I knew by heart, had heard repeated almost every Sunday for the whole of my life but, somehow, that morning it took on a new significance for me.

The chaplain was elderly and not particularly inspiring, but what he said did not really seem to be important. It was the whole atmosphere which gripped me: the starkness of the chapel, its lack of ornamentation, the grey-haired physicians in long white coats, nurses in striped uniforms of various colours, young housemen in short white coats with stethoscopes protruding from their pockets, Sisters in tall starched caps, domestic staff wearing pink overalls, all mingling with the patients in their gaudy dressing gowns. Each one was participating in the service, seemingly eager, hungry even, for what the Bible had to say to them.

I felt all around me a yearning for truth, for hope, which I had never encountered before: a reaching out in faith to some unseen force which alone could bring back joy, could restore health, could give peace.

No fiery words were pronounced, the Bible readings were all passages I had heard from my earliest days, and the hymns tried favourites I loved to sing: nothing was new and yet, that morning, everything was new.

As the chaplain raised his arms wide above the bowed heads of the congregation and pronounced the final blessing, the atmosphere of that little chapel seemed to flow through me like a healing stream. The hopes and fears of all those who had worshipped there over the years began to permeate me and I knew that I had the answer to the question I had agonised over as dawn broke that day.

I knew not only that I COULD carry on, but that I WOULD carry on, that I wanted to carry on: that there was something more for me to learn in this vast old hospital besides the technique of becoming a good nurse.

Montgomery stood up and gently put her hand under the armpit of the man sitting beside her to ease him upright.

I turned, swivelling round the wheelchair next to me in the aisle so that it faced the exit and we flowed with the throng through the heavy double doors and back into the corridor. And as we entered the lift and rose to the top floor, my spirits rose with it.

CHAPTER EIGHT

He Came to Me

Knowing that I did not have to leap smartly out of bed in the morning in answer to the strident bell, I wandered down to Jane's room when I got back to the nurses' home that evening. She had come off duty at three o'clock and had just returned from a long walk along the Embankment. Her face was flushed with the exercise and her usually impeccably dressed dark brown hair was blown awry by the gentle breeze which rose from the river.

"What a GLORIOUS evening," she said, flopping down on the bed and kicking off her shoes. "It was so gorgeous out I didn't want to come in."

I sat down in the armchair and looked across at her. Once again I was struck, as I had been that evening in the bus bringing us back from the hospital to the Old Lodge, by how much she had changed from the pale, withdrawn young woman who had come to the PTS back in March. Finally getting to grips with nursing, the real thing, seemed to have brought her out of herself and she had blossomed.

"What are you staring at?" she enquired.

"Sorry," I answered, "was I staring? Didn't mean to. I was just thinking what a change there is in you now from when we first met. You seem to have really come into your own."

She didn't say anything for a few moments, just sat reflectively on the bed, describing an unknown pattern on the carpet with her toe.

"I think I have," she said quietly.

"You've had the good luck to be with a Sister who's HUMAN," I remarked.

Jane's toe continued to go round and round on the carpet in concentric circles.

"It's not only that," she said at last and she looked up, her foot now still and poised in mid air. "You're right – I have changed, and perhaps having a Sister who is human has helped, but that isn't the whole story."

I looked across at her enquiringly.

"It's just a year ago since the Taurus went down," she said softly.

"Oh Jane," I burst out, "I'm SO sorry. I didn't mean…"

"I know you didn't," she smiled.

"Do you feel very badly?" I enquired diffidently.

She paused and bit her lip as if concentrating.

"The actual day was ghastly," she said, "I just relived every minute of it all over again."

She shrugged her shoulders expressively and I waited, not knowing what to say.

"It still hurts," she went on. "I suppose it always will, but I feel now that a page has definitely turned: I can't go on mourning for the rest of my life. Roddy was such fun, he'd have hated to see me the way I've been this past year. He was young and full of enthusiasm – he grasped life in both hands and enjoyed every minute of it. The last thing he'd have wanted was a moping wife."

She looked up and smiled.

"We made a pact just before we married. The war was still on and we were both very much in the thick of it. We promised that if anything should happen to either of us the one left would not let his or her life be shattered by it."

She paused and shrugged again.

"Of course, pacts are easy to make but, when faced with the reality… they are not so easy to keep. And I've let my side down very badly."

She looked back at her toe which was now idly describing circles in the air.

"I think it would have been easier had Roddy gone down during the war. It was the pointlessness, the utter stupidity of his dying in peacetime, on a routine voyage, which made me bitter."

"You don't SEEM bitter," I said.

"I'm not any more," she replied. "I've got through the first year and that's the worst. Now I can no longer say 'last year at this time', which is what I've been doing every day since it happened. That year's finally over and I've pledged myself to look forwards not backwards."

"I think you're very brave," I murmured.

"Do you?" she queried.

She paused reflectively, her foot now still, and a silence fell between us.

"Jane," I said hesitantly at last. "Do you believe in anything?"

She frowned.

"What do you mean?"

I bit my lip, embarrassed, not quite sure how I had got on to the subject and now that I had started, not entirely sure that I wanted to continue.

"Well, oh I don't know, in God and a hereafter I suppose."

She looked straight at me.

"If I didn't I don't think I would have survived these last twelve months," she answered quietly.

I nodded.

"Don't *you*?" she asked gently after a few minutes had passed, the silence between us only broken by loud shrieks of laughter coming from the room next door.

"I don't know," I answered slowly.

Then it all came pouring out.

"I thought I did, but now I'm not sure. All my life I've gone to church, done what I thought was the right thing and never really questioned anything at all, but in the last year or so everything has come up for review in my mind and I can't help wondering what it's all about, why we're here, what's the purpose. At least, that's how I felt until this morning."

I got up and walked to the window, looking down onto the empty courtyard below.

"Today Sister sent me with some patients to the service in the chapel and there I had this strange feeling that there WAS a reason, perhaps even a reason for all this suffering, that there was a hope. It was almost is if everything clicked into place in my mind... though not quite."

Jane looked across at me and frowned.

"I was at the service in the chapel this morning," she said, "and I must say I didn't find it very inspiring. I wonder what it was that touched you?"

"I don't know," I said quietly, turning from the window and flopping back down into the armchair. "I agree with you, it WASN'T terribly inspiring but there was just something there, something indefinable."

And we lapsed once more into silence.

"If it happens to you as it happened to me, this knowing beyond a doubt that there IS a God and that He cares," Jane said softly, "you'll find that there is no special time or place for us to meet Him; He comes to each one of us in our own time. Perhaps that service in the chapel this morning was your time?"

I didn't answer. I didn't know.

"He came to me," she went on, her voice hardly above a whisper, "at the point of my deepest need... and I praise Him for it."

I looked up at her in amazement. I had never heard her speak like that before and certainly never heard God spoken of as a person, someone who comes to us, someone who cares. In my mind He had always been rather remote, a being who lived 'up there', not a God with whom we could have any direct contact. Her statement had shattered me and I couldn't think of anything to say.

"It's not much fun being a widow," Jane murmured reflectively, almost as if she were talking to herself, "and at first I couldn't accept it. I felt amputated, as if half of me had been torn away and I'd been left shocked and bleeding. Then when I lost the baby I became very bitter."

She paused.

"It was then that I had this meeting with Jesus and discovered that there IS a plan for our lives. It's not all a game of chance, there is a pattern even if we can't understand it at the time. I know now that God cares and that He chose me for a purpose.

"But what possible purpose could there be in taking your husband away like that?" I burst out.

"I don't know," she answered gently. "I'll probably never know until I meet Him face to face, but it's a question I asked myself over and over again after Roddy died."

She looked across at me, her beautiful dark blue eyes soft and luminous.

"That's probably why you said earlier on that I'd changed since we first met," she said softly. "Although I was a committed Christian when I arrived at the PTS, I think I was still torturing myself with questions, endlessly asking why."

She smiled.

"And I didn't find any answer."

"Have you found one now?" I enquired.

"Not really," she went on. "But in these last few months my faith has settled and jelled as it were, and I'm at peace."

She paused.

"I've found Jesus," she said at last, "and for the moment I'm content just to trust."

I took a deep breath. It all sounded so incredible.

"You said earlier on that I didn't seem bitter," she continued.

I nodded.

"You wouldn't have said that a year ago. I was just eaten up with bitterness and resentment... and self-pity. Then I met a woman in hospital when I lost the baby. She was one of the volunteer helpers. You know the sort of people, we have them here: they bring trolleys round the wards with soap, writing paper, library books and the like."

I nodded again.

"She used to sit and talk to me and when I left she invited me to her home to convalesce. Ursula was a lovely person who didn't try to give me all the answers, she just listened. She let all the anguish and bitterness pour out and in the end, she led me to Jesus."

Jane paused and seemed to be very far away.

"Now I walk and talk with Him every day," she said softly.

I don't know whether I was more embarrassed or curious at Jane's revelations, but she had awakened a hunger in me and I needed to know more.

"Is that what you were doing in the PTS garden every

morning before breakfast?" I enquired diffidently.

"Yes," she answered. "It's a habit I got into while staying with Ursula. God felt very near during those weeks in her home: the whole place seemed to be soaked in peace and tranquillity." She leant back on the bed and pushed a pillow under her head.

"Her husband and her son had both gone down in the war and yet she had this wonderful serenity. She was completely without bitterness and I knew that she had something which I desperately needed... and wanted. We spent hours just talking and gradually her peace began to flow into me and I came to accept what had happened."

I looked at her in amazement.

"Not to UNDERSTAND," she emphasised, "but to accept, and with acceptance comes peace. Ursula had been a nurse in the first World War when she met her husband who was in the regular Navy, so, in a way, I suppose I identified with her. He was a surgeon-captain when he went down in '42 and her twenty-year-old son went down just ten months later. Enough to make anyone bitter... but she wasn't."

Jane paused and a smile played round her lips. "When we met, Ursula was completely alone, just like me," she said softly. "Only she had Jesus. And until I met her, I didn't, just a dreadful aching emptiness which I'd filled with self-pity and bitterness. But Ursula showed me that many of the tragedies in our lives for which we blame God are not what He had planned for us: they are caused by men."

She looked across at me.

"This war wasn't His idea, was it?"

"If He's all-powerful He could have stopped it, or even prevented it happening at all," I said vehemently.

Jane smiled.

"He could have, but He didn't, because in creating us He made us free, free to choose good or evil. Unfortunately, the war was caused by men who chose evil."

"And millions of innocent people suffered," I said bitterly.

Jane didn't immediately reply and I watched her like a tiger waiting to pounce.

"God suffered too," she said quietly at last. "Like any loving father suffers when he sees his children taking the wrong path."

I sat in tight-lipped silence.

"In a lesser way I'm sure now that my mother suffered when she waved goodbye to me as I left on the ship bringing me to wartime Britain," Jane went on. "Maybe SHE thought I was making the wrong choice: I didn't HAVE to come, but she gave me the freedom to choose my own life and didn't try to prevent me."

I was slowly beginning to understand.

"The way things have turned out, she probably wishes she had. It can't be easy for her being so far away, knowing that her only child has been so badly hurt. But she hasn't stopped loving me because I chose to go my own way. I know that all last year she was suffering right there beside me, not saying 'I told you so'."

Jane's voice had dropped almost to a whisper.

"That's the way Jesus loves us, unconditionally. In all loving there is always an element of suffering and sometimes the more we love, the more we suffer."

She looked across at me and her eyes were moist.

"If I hadn't loved Roddy so much I don't suppose I would have suffered so much. But I wouldn't have wanted to have loved him less in spite of the suffering it caused."

A solitary tear trickled slowly down her cheek.

"That's what God does," she whispered, her voice almost inaudible. "He suffers right along beside us like my mother did. I know because I've felt His presence and been comforted and uplifted by it."

She smiled across at me.

"It would be SO much easier for Him just to use us like puppets on a string and pull us out of any hurtful situation but, just like any loving earthly parent, He respects our free will, knowing full well what it will cost Him."

"But what's the POINT of all this suffering?" I broke in, ending aggressively, "I think I'd rather be a puppet."

Jane smiled affectionately at me.

"You wouldn't, you know," she continued, now

completely in control of her emotions. "Just imagine what it would be like to have every decision made for you, or even changed and snatched out of your control once you'd made it; every movement or initiative hampered. You'd soon scream with frustration."

I shrugged, not entirely convinced.

"Might be better than the dreadful pain," I muttered.

Jane shook her head and smiled again.

"I once felt like that too," she murmured. "But during those weeks with Ursula I think I touched the depth of suffering, yet she showed me that suffering is a fact of life: we can't escape it, EVERYONE experiences it to some degree at some point in their lives."

She paused.

"It all depends on what one does with it," she ended.

I opened my mouth to protest but she stopped me.

"I know what you're going to say, because I've said it all too. Why do some people have to suffer so much?"

I nodded.

"I wish I had the answer to that question, but I haven't. Our sufferings are not meant to separate us from God but to bring us back to Him when everything else we depend on has failed."

Jane looked out of the window at nothing in particular.

"If I didn't believe THAT," she went on, "life down here wouldn't make any sense at all."

She turned round to look at me, her eyes shining.

"Jesus constantly taught that the best was yet to come, that His kingdom is characterised by hope, the 'hope of glory'. That's not a sop to the suffering of the present, but the context which gives our suffering significance and perspective."

The tightness inside me was gradually loosening its grip. The idea that someone, even if that someone was not actually there with us physically, UNDERSTOOD the pain and, because He understood, could really comfort us, was an idea I longed to grasp hold of. The aggression tangled up inside me was slowly beginning to unravel and the desire to know more, not just to oppose everything she said, was gradually taking over.

"Does believing really help?" I whispered.

Jane nodded slowly.

"As I devoured the Bible during those days in Ursula's garden," she went on, "Jesus showed me that suffering can do two things: it can either ennoble us or embitter us. And it was embittering me."

She laughed.

"Not that I've made anything very noble out of it since I turned to Him, but at least I'm not bitter any more: I'm not all twisted inside and eaten up by it as I was then."

"Was it surprising?" I muttered.

"Surprising, no," she cut in. "Stupid, yes. I was only hurting myself even more, keeping the wound open, even causing it to go septic instead of letting it slowly heal."

"Does it ever heal?" I asked grimly.

"Yes it does," she answered gently, "in time."

She leant back on the bed and gazed up at the ceiling.

"If we let it," she continued softly, "but not if we insist on keeping it open and infected by pouring poison into it. And that's what I was doing: refusing to let the healing process begin."

She paused reflectively.

"I think in a way I was afraid to let it heal: I felt that it was a betrayal of Roddy to even imagine that I could ever be whole again. And so I refused to face reality, to accept what had happened and come to terms with it."

She leaned up on one elbow and looked across at me.

"I was refusing to forgive," she said simply.

"Forgive?" I echoed. "How CAN you forgive?"

"I couldn't," she said. "I blamed and hated everybody."

She smiled and her eyes were still moist.

"But I can now. It happened when I took Jesus at His word. No one can forgive terrible hurts in their own strength but He promised to pour His love and His strength into our weakness. He said He would carry our burdens and this one was too heavy for me to bear, so I took my pain and my bitterness and gave them to Him. And when I did that He showed me that we cannot wipe out the past, but that He can heal the hurt it has left behind."

She pushed a pillow into place and leant back on the bed again.

"Through His love," she went on softly, "instead of being constantly overwhelmed by grief, I was gradually able to move away from that time of suffering. I was able to acknowledge the unfairness of what had happened to me, what had happened to so many women in the last few years, look the injustice and the hurt full in the face, accept Roddy's death, not try to pretend it wasn't painful, and forgive. And in doing so I was able to cut a growing malignant tumour out of my life and let the healing begin."

I shook my head in disbelief.

Jane stretched and took a deep breath.

"Now I'm FREE," she said at last, her voiced poised and steady. "Free to start again, a different life, but a new life... as a whole liberated person, instead of the spiritual cripple I used to be."

More gusts of hysterical laughter burst from the room next door and we both smiled, wondering what on earth Rachel and Bunty were up to.

"Ursula taught me not to waste my suffering but to put it to good use."

She swung her long slim legs over the side of the bed.

"And that's what I intend to do," she said. "She showed me that God CAN bring good out of evil, if only we will let Him."

Jane smiled to herself, obviously remembering those precious days in her friend's sunny garden.

"And I want to let Him," she ended softly.

CHAPTER NINE

Jacques

As I sat still in a rather bewildered silence, trying to collect my thoughts, wanting to ask her how I, too, could have this assurance, this personal contact with a God who was there, the telephone rang shrilly in the hall outside and I heard the patter of slippered feet pass Jane's door as someone went to answer it.

"I still think you're very brave," I murmured at last, almost to myself. All the other words I had wanted to say had stuck in my throat and refused to come out. "And, in a way, I envy you."

Before she could reply there was a sharp tap on the door and Bunty's tousled golden head appeared round it. "Thought I'd find you here," she grinned. "Saw you come off the bus so knew you couldn't be far."

She paused and her impish face lit up.

"Did you see ME?"

We shook our heads, puzzled.

"I missed the bus and arrived back here before any of you."

Her eyes sparkled.

"You'll never guess how!"

Intrigued, we had both now quite forgotten why she had knocked on the door in the first place.

"I got a LIFT," she said, coming in and leaning her back against the door as if to prevent anyone overhearing her secret, "in a POLICE LAUNCH."

She paused for further dramatic effect.

"It was gorgeous," she gurgled, her eyes rolling ecstatically round and round, "such bronzed, brawny, handsome young men. They were patrolling the river."

She stopped and her eyes stopped too and focused

intently on us as she took a deep breath before making her final thrust.

"I think they were looking for a BODY."

"Oh Bunty," I laughed, "You read too many women's magazines."

Then suddenly remembering that there must have been some other reason for her appearance I asked:

"What did you want me for by the way?"

"Oh, I forgot. Telephone."

She tapped her forehead exasperatedly with one finger.

"I'm SO scatter-brained. Just had a ghastly row with Rachel because I drop everything on the floor so I flung her suspender belt, which just happened to be on the floor too, out of the window and it landed in a tree. We were trying to poke it back with a stick when the 'phone rang. Morley-Watson got quite ratty when I yelled up the stairs for you. I think she saw me being handed off the launch by three Tarzans and got jealous... or perhaps I was just interrupting her evening devotions, now that she's got no old bones to chew over."

"You really are the end," I interrupted, "was the call for me?"

"Oh yes it was," she said, "forgot again. I think it's Charles Boyer."

I frowned in surprise as I got up.

"Bunty," I said exasperatedly, "who is it really?"

"It's a MAN," she gurgled, rolling her eyes all over again. She really had the most expressively wicked blue eyes I had ever seen. "With a gorgeous foreign accent."

More puzzled than ever I walked towards the door she was now holding open for me.

"You're a dark horse," she went on, her eyes continuing to swivel round and round in her head in a most perilous fashion. "Never told us you had a Latin lover up your sleeve."

"Oh Bunty," I laughed pushing past her, vaguely wondering whether the unknown Latin lover had had the patience to hold on, "you're IMPOSSIBLE."

"Ask him if he's got a friend who's a curate for ME," she

shouted as I walked along the corridor and picked up the phone.

"Never thought I'd manage to track you down," the foreign voice came down the line with a hint of laughter in it. "What have you been up to? Tried everywhere and finally had to ring your parents to discover your whereabouts."

"Jacques," I answered in surprise. "Where are you?"

"About ten minutes away," he laughed.

"But I thought you were in New York?"

"I thought YOU were in London."

"Well I am," I laughed in reply.

"Yes but not where I expected you to be."

"What are you doing over here?"

"I'm on business," he replied. "A rushed trip. Got a meeting tomorrow and take the Night Ferry back."

"The Night Ferry?" I echoed. "Are you in Paris again?"

"For the time being," he replied. "But when can we meet? Are you free now?"

"Er... NOW?" I demurred.

"Yes now," he laughed. "I haven't had dinner yet, can you join me?"

I hesitated, not knowing quite what to say. It was already past nine and we had a ten o'clock curfew which could not be broken without prior permission and then never on a working day. How could I explain all this to Jacques? He'd never understand, none of my former friends would: it would merely confirm their theory that I needed my head examined.

"I'm afraid I've had dinner," I answered, clutching that as an excuse, "and I've just come off duty after an exhausting day. Perhaps tomorrow? It's my day off as it happens."

"Splendid," Jacques replied. "I shall be busy until about six or so but we can have dinner before I leave if you're free."

"Lovely," I breathed. I hadn't seen Jacques since he left for the States and it would be good to renew contact with him again.

"I'll pick you up around seven," he ended. "Where exactly ARE you by the way?"

"Oh don't bother," I replied.

How could I tell him that men, even brothers, were not allowed inside the nurses' home? I was already wondering how I was going to face him, wondering what he would think of the new me, now so subdued and submissive.

"I'll just meet you somewhere in town," I went on. "This place is a bit out of the way and I don't know exactly what I shall be doing tomorrow."

"Just as you wish," he replied. "I'll book a table at the Albert for seven. It's not far from Victoria so we can catch up on what's been happening until the last minute. Hope you'll recognise me, I'm beginning to lose my hair."

"I can't believe it," I laughed.

Jacques had always had a mass of light brown hair which curled over his ears and fell in an unruly mop over his forehead and often into his eyes.

"It's true," he sighed, "old age catches up with all of us in the end."

And we both laughed.

Bunty's head appeared round the door of their unspeakably untidy room as I put the receiver down. She was waving a pink suspender belt on the end of a hockey stick.

"Got it," she said triumphantly, holding it up to view. "I've been listening... and you DIDN'T ask him if his cousin's a curate."

"Oh Bunty, shut up," I said irritably, and as her pretty cherubic face dropped in surprise and suddenly looked woebegone, I immediately regretted my sudden burst of temper.

But as I turned to apologise, wondering what on earth had caused me to reply so snappily, she had already withdrawn her head and shut the door. I shrugged my shoulders and walked towards the stairs, my mind and my thoughts awhirl with the successive shocks which had bombarded them in the past twenty-four hours.

On reflection, I was not entirely sure I had done the right thing in accepting Jacques' invitation to dinner. My past life had started to recede and become remote and yet here I was, about to resurrect it again.

"Oh well," I murmured to myself as I began to climb to the fifth floor. "He's leaving tomorrow night, so it's only a glimpse of the past, a slight lifting of the curtain and then back to the grind again. There'll be no harm done."

Going into my room, I was suddenly conscious how weary I was. I shut the door and, without meaning to or even realising it, shut out the memory of all that had happened that day, even my conversation with Jane which had so touched me. It was almost as if, the veil having at last been lifted so that the answer was almost within my grasp, it had suddenly fallen back into place again. And as it did so the doubts, the queries and the questions came hurtling back.

* * * * * *

I needn't have worried about my meeting with Jacques. The few hours we spent together before he had to run for his train were a panacea: he was kind and understanding and, unlike most of my other friends, didn't think I had gone berserk.

We had first met early in 1946 when he arrived from Paris to work for the BBC, which I had joined a few months earlier. When he left to go to New York eighteen months later we had kept in touch by Christmas card. I was pleased to link up with him again: he was not at all the typical caricature of the excitable Frenchman, being gentle and reserved and more of a listener than a talker: in fact just what I needed at that point in time.

As we sat together in the quiet intimate restaurant, to my surprise I found myself telling him not only about my new life, but about the doubts I occasionally had as to the wisdom of having taken such a step after so many years of independence: doubts which I had never voiced to any of my other friends.

He didn't interrupt me but, when I had finished, said very quietly:

"I can only say how much I admire you for what you're doing. I had no idea you had left the BBC, so it was a surprise when your mother told me that you had taken this step. But congratulations. Don't give up, I'm sure you'll make a wonderful nurse."

I wasn't sure Sister would agree with him, and told him so.

"It's early days yet," he smiled. "Don't worry, your sense of humour will see you through."

As the taxi which had dropped Jacques at Victoria Station – only just in time – slid along the Embankment, I watched the mid-summer twilight fall like a soft blanket over the smooth waters of the Thames, and I pondered over what he had said. I couldn't see myself becoming a wonderful nurse, a wonderful anything, at that moment. In fact, all the reports I had had about my bright and shining future since I entered the PTS had pointed to the contrary. But Jacques' words had been encouraging and I was grateful for his gentleness, his kindness and his understanding – and above all, for his complete lack of judgement as to what I should or should not do.

I had had so much negative advice in the past year since my decision had been taken, mostly from people I cared about and whose opinion I respected, that I had sometimes begun to wonder myself whether I had not completely taken leave of my senses. But Jacques had been different. All he had said had been so very positive and helpful.

As the waters of that great river darkened, the last lingering flecks of light left the sky and night fell over London, I once again experienced that feeling of purpose, almost of destiny, which had so abruptly left me the evening before, slowly flowing back to fill my whole being with a sense of anticipation tinged with joy. I was drenched with a peace and an assurance that there was someone in control and that all the strands of my life so far – my decision to train as a nurse, my friendship with Jane, that strange 'something' I had encountered in the chapel that morning and my meeting with Jacques – were all part of a tapestry, the strands of which were already being woven together to form the whole and give me the answer as to why I was here.

Little did I then realise that out of that pattern, that tapestry, Jacques would emerge as my husband.

CHAPTER TEN

Not Entirely by Chance

Jacques' unexpected visit had been like a breath of fresh air blowing into a sick room. I didn't realise at the time just how much I needed his encouragement and yet, when I awoke the next morning, it was with a feeling of lightness and expectation, of pleasure when thinking of the day ahead.

It was a day much like any other day, filled with hot dusting, dirty linen to be scrubbed, bandages to be wound, gauze dressing squares to be folded, meals to be handed out and patients to be fussed over and made comfortable, but I sailed through it with a song in my heart and a lightness in my step. Even Sister didn't loom quite so large and formidable and for once I didn't seem to be a permanent thorn in her flesh.

"Nurse," she squeaked in my direction towards the end of the morning. "Put the screens round Mr. Briggs, he's first on the afternoon list, and get him into his operation gown and socks. Afterwards, I'll show you how to give him his pre-med."

Then I really trembled.

I had never given an injection, though theoretically I knew exactly how to do it. But actually plunging a needle into real flesh instead of an orange was a terrifying prospect, and I'd have preferred to do it in the company of anyone rather than Sister.

Yet, in spite of my clammy shaking fingers, he didn't give an agonised yell and her nod of approval as we straightened the sheet and went out from behind the green-curtained screens was worth more to me than an OBE.

Looking back now, I realise that Sister probably had a communication problem which was beyond her control: a shyness and a sensitivity about her height and her beanstalk figure which she attempted to hide behind a gruff exterior. And also, what a responsibility it must have been in a busy surgical ward to have a raw inexperienced student nurse thrust upon her every three months. All things considered, I wonder how she even managed to remain as civil with me as she did.

As I slipped into my new daily routine, observing and absorbing life in the raw through close contact with patients whose outer veneer had been stripped away through anxiety, pain and suffering, learning each day under the experienced hand of Sister and those senior to me more and more nursing skills, the months flew by without my noticing it. The end of September, when we would all change our wards and move on to another experience, suddenly arrived. I was quite looking forward to this, confident that everything else would continue as before: I would remain in the little fifth floor room with the splendid view which I had come to love, and still be surrounded by the friends I had made at PTS.

The day the changes were announced I was late off duty and hurried down to the narrow corridor outside Matron's office where the list was pinned up. All my set were crowded round it, frilly muslin caps bobbing up and down as nurses jockeyed for position, seeking to discover their fate.

Morley-Watson was turning away as I arrived.

"Oh hallo Baxter," she barked, her nose twitching as she wriggled her glasses back into position. "You're going to the Annexe. So am I."

She announced it as if it were good news.

"The Annexe," I gasped. "Oh NO! Let me see."

And I pushed forward towards the notice-board.

But there was no mistake. There was my name and there was the one word it had never occurred to me to find opposite it: Annexe. I hadn't dreaded it because, for some inexplicable reason, I had never even entertained it as a possibility. I had rather hoped for one of the children's wards, but hadn't really minded where they sent me: after my training with my present Sister ANYWHERE would have been a picnic, I thought. But the ANNEXE. I groaned and remained standing in front of the list, speechless and unable to move.

I looked down towards Jane's name, hoping against hope that she would be coming too but no, she had got what I wanted: Children's Surgical.

My lips tightened as I turned away, full of self-pity and rebellion. Why, why did I have to be sent to the Annexe, AND with Morley-Watson too: and for a split second I thought of resigning. I just could not face the prospect of burying myself down there in the wilds all winter, miles from anywhere. Tears smarted behind my eyes and threatened to overflow as I brushed past the gaggle of nurses who were all eagerly discussing their prospects, bumping into Donaldson as I did so.

"We're going to be together," she said and her freckled face broke into a smile.

I looked up blankly.

"You going to Belsen too?" I asked grimly.

"Oh, don't take it like that," she laughed. "It could be worse."

"Could it?" I replied and turned away.

I hadn't had much to do with Donaldson since that first day in PTS when we had scrubbed baths together, but she seemed a pleasant person and for a fraction of a second, my spirits rose: then the memory of the Annexe, those grim improvised huts put up in haste during the war when the hospital had been evacuated to the country, rose up in my mind, and they immediately descended to zero.

Walking back into the long main hall, I suddenly felt unable to face all that excited chatter and decided I didn't want lunch. I walked through one of the side doors and paced up and down outside the hospital entrance, angry with the Sisters in Matron's office who had decided on my fate, angry at fate for having let them make such a decision, angry at myself for having been so idiotic as ever to come to this benighted hole. All the peace and sense of purpose which had sustained me during the last few months suddenly evaporated, leaving in its wake a seething mass of fury, resentment and self-pity.

Climbing into the bus to go back to the nurses' home for my few hours off after lunch, I was glad Jane was not free. I didn't want to see her. I felt angry at her too, blaming her quite irrationally for the office's decision in her favour: she was to stay in London and go to the ward I had hoped for. And, once again, those petty, self-pitying words swirled round and round in my brain: 'It's not fair!'

Mercifully, I was left alone. Most of the nurses in the bus were not my set and those who were obviously thought that if I wanted to sit by myself looking like a thunder cloud, they would let me. And they did.

* * * * * *

Lying miserably on my bed, gazing up at the ceiling, my angry feelings gradually began to recede and I saw that no one was to blame. Perhaps after all, it wouldn't be as bad as I had imagined. There wasn't ONLY Morley-Watson going, there was Donaldson and quite a few others. I could always come up to town on my day off and meet Jane, I thought, quite forgetting that the chances of our days off coinciding were infinitesimal.

By the time four o'clock came and the tea bell sounded, my anger had subsided and I was able to face the world again. I was also very hungry and ran down to the dining room to devour slice after slice of bread and marge before returning to the hospital and the evening work-load.

There had been ten operations in the ward that day so once back, I didn't have much time to indulge my misery but was kept scurrying round until the chimes of Big Ben sounded nine and I joined thankfully with the rest of the day staff to report and go off duty.

Walking towards the bus I saw Jane waiting for me.

"I'm SO sorry about the Annexe," she said sympathetically as we got in and sat down together.

"Oh, it could have been worse," I answered grimly. "Though not much. But it's jolly good luck for you."

She grimaced.

"I feel rather guilty," she said.

"Why should you?" I asked, almost aggressively.

"Well, you going off to the Annexe and me getting such a plum."

I laughed.

"Well, I must say, you HAVE been rather lucky. TWO plums in a row. But, never fear, your turn will come."

"I'd ask to change with someone and come to the Annexe with you," she went on. "But I know it would never be allowed."

"You're darned right it wouldn't," I said, and we lapsed into silence.

"I'm going to miss you," she said as we parted at the second floor.

"Me too," I answered and went on up.

I didn't want to talk. I didn't want to gather for a cosy chat and a cup of cocoa before lights out as most of the others were doing. I'd had a tiring day but, above all, my resentment had drained me.

Entering the little room which had become my home, a wave of anguish swept over me. It was a haven which represented security and peace – things I had lost when I plunged myself into this new adventure earlier in the year – and I didn't want to give it up. Suddenly my tiredness, on top of every other emotion I had indulged in since lunchtime, overwhelmed me. Throwing myself on the bed I sobbed, great silent gusts of pain heaving up from deep within me: sobs which were out of all proportion to the reason for which I was crying. They hid something deeper which I was unable at that moment to express, didn't even realise I was feeling. A hunger, a searching, a reaching out which had touched the surface so many times in the past few months and then dipped below again.

But the tears were cleansing and, when I finally rolled over and looked out of the window at the darkness beyond and saw the thin silver streak of the river as it flowed endlessly by, I felt the peace which I had temporarily lost come gently flowing back into my tired mind. Wearily I dragged myself from the bed, cold and stiff but no longer full of anger and bitterness.

I didn't know why I was being sent to the Annexe. I knew of course that I was merely a name on a list, that there was nothing personal in the selection: I happened to be at the beginning of the alphabet, the other end would go later. But I had taken it personally, as an affront, a revenge, and I now realised my own stupidity. As I did so I laughed, but the house was silent and my laugh seemed to echo round it like a piercing shriek.

Pulling off my clothes I fell into bed, momentarily appeased, and though still not overjoyed by the change which was about to disrupt my life, I had a strange feeling that it was not entirely by chance that this decision had been made; that a powerful, unseen hand had been in command and had had more than a say in this next move on the chess board of my life.

CHAPTER ELEVEN

I Want to Get Home to My Baby

When I finally closed the door on the little room which had come to mean so much to me, I felt that yet another chapter was closing in my life. The bed stripped, the drawers and cupboards empty, the photographs and little knick-knacks which had given it that personal touch removed, the room looked abandoned and forlorn.

It was raining when we clambered into the bus waiting to take us to the Annexe, which did nothing to raise my spirits. An hour and a half later when we finally arrived, the rain had turned into a storm. We stepped down on to soggy earth, with great gusts of wind blowing us in all directions.

The collection of tin huts and makeshift wards, with the cold concrete paths meandering between them, appeared even more drab then I had remembered. We had visited the Annexe during our PTS time but it had been on a bright May afternoon and, despite its resemblance to a prisoner-of-war camp, it had not seemed as desolate as it did today.

As we clutched our cloaks around us, attempting to hold our caps in position against the wind, the Sister in charge of the nurses' home appeared at the door.

'Appeared' is an understatement. Being the same height as the Sister I had just bidden goodbye, only broader, she towered in the doorway, almost completely blocking it. Her thick flaming red hair, generously streaked with grey, which floated in wisps around her ears, was tucked into an untidy bun beneath her tall cap. Her steel rimmed glasses were held together by khaki wool, and her legs, which appeared to have been stuck on upside down, were encased in black woollen hand-knitted stockings, ending abruptly in the most enormous pair of regulation shoes I had ever seen. They looked like herring boxes.

She flung the door wide open, so that the rain lashed in.

"Welcome," she boomed, her shiny red face grinning broadly. "I've got the kettle on. Tea's ready."

And we all stumbled higgledy piggledy behind her as she stamped ahead into her little room where the inevitable thick slices of bread and marge were heaped untidily onto a plate.

Everything about Home Sister, as she was called, was large as life and twice as eccentric. She was quite a legend in the hospital and we all knew that she was one of the few surviving members of a very old, aristocratic Irish family most of whom had, over the centuries, rushed off and done unusual or terribly daring things during successive wars, won lots of battle honours for bravery and mostly never returned. Her brother, who had somehow managed to escape the massacre and now lived alone in the family castle, had a passion for railways and quite often helped the stoker on the little local train or ran up and down the platform of the country station bearing his family's name, pushing a luggage trolley or blowing the whistle.

This latter idiosyncrasy not infrequently caused panic and confusion, since he invariably blew it at the wrong time sending passengers scuttling chaotically in every direction as trains which were not supposed to stop screeched to an unexpected halt whilst others tore off without warning before those alighting had had time to get out and those waiting on the platform had had a chance to get in, leaving bewildered faces at carriage windows and angry scuffles in the guard's van.

Sister was an equally colourful character with equally weird habits.

She kept the coal for our stove, the only means of heating the hut, in the bath together with her gardening tools, and grew chives and radishes under her bedroom window. Years earlier, after finishing her training, she had gone to nurse in India and once boomed out to us, in a moment of confidence:

"In an emergency, Nurses, all you need to deliver a baby is a pile of newspapers, an old macintosh, a piece of string and a pair of scissors." She had apparently delivered babies in grass huts and steaming jungles, in the corridors of non-stop trains snaking all over the Indian continent as well as other highly unlikely places: though she omitted to mention how many of them actually survived!

Many of the girls training with me had double-barrelled names but Sister's was treble-barrelled and even in those more leisurely immediate post-war years took far too long to pronounce so, adopting the custom of past generations of student nurses, we called her Gert. As she towered over the enormous tea-pot that rainy autumn afternoon, her face one huge smile above her whiskery chin, my sagging spirits slowly began to revive.

Once we had swilled down the steaming orange brew and consumed numerous thick slices of bread and marge – I was beginning to be seriously concerned about my former trim waistline, but at that moment was too hungry to care – Sister stomped off down the corridor which ran down the middle of the hut.

Flinging back the dark green curtains which flanked either side, so that the rings rattled angrily against the rails, she revealed to each one of us in turn the small oblong cubicle which was to be our home for the next few months.

I was lucky as I was shown into the first cubicle. This at least had a solid wall on one side, providing some slight protection from the giggling and endless hubbub which went on non-stop down the central aisle. The other dividing walls were paper thin and, as only a curtain shut off each cubicle, any privacy was out of the question.

"When you've unpacked," Sister boomed, "change your aprons and I'll show you to your wards. Assemble at five to five. Bathrooms here."

She crashed open two or three doors in explanation and slammed off.

When we assembled, as instructed, at five to five, she looked us over, marched to the head of the queue, swirled her left arm round her head like the pitcher in an American baseball game and brought it down in a horizontal position, one finger pointing directly in front of her indicating the direction we were to follow.

Then taking three-foot strides, obviously imagining she was still tramping through a snake-infested jungle, she set off purposefully with all of us scrambling behind in an attempt to keep up. I half expected her to blow an ear splitting blast on a trumpet and yell:

"Into battle! Follow me, men!"

I was one of the last recruits in the battalion to be dropped off. As we approached the end hut, Sister swung her left arm in another semi-circular movement and pointed. I gathered that my base for the next few months was to be Women's Medical, so dropped out of the marching line and walked down the sloping concrete path to the ward door.

As had happened in London only a few months earlier, no one appeared to be breathlessly awaiting my arrival and I hovered in the entrance not quite knowing what to do next. While I was hesitating, the door opened from the other side and I almost collided with a tall, dark-haired young man wearing a clerical collar.

He smiled.

"I'm SO sorry Nurse," he said apologetically, standing aside to let me pass.

I smiled back and the door closed, leaving me at the entrance to a small makeshift ward, narrower than the one I had been used to in London, with a coal-burning stove hissing contentedly in the middle.

"Oh there you are nurse."

The Ward Sister looked up from the bedside of a young woman who had obviously just been admitted. Her suitcase was perched on the locker and a man I took to be her husband was standing beside her holding her hand.

"Do telephone later this evening to put your mind at rest Mr. Forrest," Sister said as she detached herself and walked over towards me. "The doctor will be coming in to see your wife shortly, but don't worry, we'll soon have the pain under control and be able to make her comfortable."

He looked up and smiled diffidently then, bending to kiss the woman in the bed, he gave her hand a final squeeze, picked up the suitcase and left the ward.

Sister turned to me.

"Mrs. Forrest has just been admitted, nurse," she said. "She had a fall a few weeks ago which has jolted her back and she is in considerable pain. I want you to make her a cup of tea while she's waiting for the RAP to come and examine her. I'm just going to hear the report and then you and Nurse Chambers can start the bed-making."

(The RAP was the Resident Assistant Physician.)

I looked at her in a panic, not knowing where anything was, not least the kitchen.

Sister looked across at me. She was of average height, neat, trim and virginal. I took her to be about forty.

"The set-up is exactly the same as in London, nurse," she answered my unspoken question. "Kitchen on the right as you come in. Now go along and make that cup of tea; Mrs. Forrest needs reassuring."

I scuttled to the kitchen, returning a few minutes later with the tray. All the nurses were standing round Sister's table in the middle of the ward giving the afternoon report and, not knowing what else to do while I waited for the unknown Nurse Chambers to reveal herself, I stood by Mrs. Forrest's bed as she drank her tea.

She sipped absently, her thoughts obviously elsewhere.

"We're two new girls," I joked, for want of something better to say.

She looked up enquiringly over the rim of her cup.

"I've just arrived," I went on, "like you."

She nodded, but didn't comment.

"What happened?" I enquired.

"I slipped," she answered quietly and her voice was soft and modulated, so soft that I had to bend over in order to hear. "In a taxi, of all things. I got up to leave and for some reason he jerked forward and threw me back on the seat."

She eased herself slightly in the bed as I took the cup from her hand, gazing enviously at the two digestive biscuits left untouched on the plate.

"It didn't hurt at the time," she went on, "but a few days later…"

She winced.

"Does it hurt now?" I enquired.

"A little," she replied. "But nothing like it has been."

She leant gingerly back on the mound of pillows.

"I feel rather a fraud," she said, "taking up a bed just because I've got a pain in my back."

"Oh, I'm sure there's a reason," I assured her warmly.

She nodded her head vaguely and I thought how frail she looked. Her face was pale and her long dark hair fell softly round it, but her eyes seemed to be almost too large against the finely chiselled cheekbones.

"I hope they discover what it is quickly," she went on, "I want to get home to my baby."

She looked down and smoothed the top of the sheet reflectively.

"He'll be a year old in two weeks' time and I don't want to miss his first birthday: it's rather special."

Her eyes wandered away, looking across the ward at nothing in particular. And as she did so, suddenly, inexplicably, an immense sadness, almost like a premonition, washed over me and I was pleased when Nurse Chambers came over and we went off together to start the evening bed-making routine.

CHAPTER TWELVE

Would You Wish to Know?

The sound of a cock crowing in the distance broke into my sleep much as the screeching of the bell had done six months earlier on my first morning at the PTS. As I slowly surfaced and opened my eyes in the unfamiliar surroundings, I once again rolled over and squinted at my watch. I saw with a start that it was ten minutes past six and I panicked: the bus would be leaving in five minutes.

Then I fell back on my pillows, remembering: I was no longer in London. I smiled to myself, realising that one of the advantages of my exile was that, there being no bus to catch, the rising bell would be delayed by at least half an hour.

I turned over and tried to go back to sleep but the unusual silence, the absolute stillness all around, was disconcerting; no distant rumble of traffic, no eerie siren coming from the boats going up and down the river, just a faint rustle as the early morning breeze stirred through the falling leaves. Leaning up on one elbow I gazed through the window as the first faint glimmer of dawn rose above the jungle of huts which stretched into the distance. I realised that for the next few months, for the whole of the winter in fact, I would eat in a hut, sleep in a hut, nurse in a hut, even go to church in a hut: and it reminded me once again of the war and the cramped conditions in the hastily constructed Anderson air-raid shelters.

Lying there my mind went back to the evening before and to Mrs. Forrest. I was still perturbed by the strange feeling of apprehension which had overwhelmed me as I stood by her bedside, and I wondered what today would bring for her.

Suddenly a door crashed open, followed by the thud of

Sister's enormous rubber-soled shoes. A harsh metallic clanging rang deafeningly through the hut as she marched up and down the central aisle, swinging a cumbersome old brass bell in her hand. As if the bell weren't enough warning, her voice boomed out: "Time to get up nurses, rise and shine."

Then she disappeared back through the swing doors which separated her quarters from ours, the horrendous clanging being immediately replaced by the early morning news wheezing out from her old-fashioned wireless set. And I knew that that precious moment of peace was over for another day as curtains were thrust aside sending the rings dancing along the rails, slippered feet padded up and down the main corridor and sleepy voices called to one another from cubicle to cubicle.

I walked with Donaldson from the dining hut through the early morning freshness, the dew still clinging to the strips of grass which ran in between the concrete paths. We breathed deeply, drinking in the sweet damp air before parting at the end of the line of huts. As I turned left to Women's Medical, she turned right to go up the slope to Men's Surgical.

As I went in, the man in clerical black who had held the door open for me the evening before was sitting alone on a small bench just inside the entrance, an attaché case resting on his knees. He looked up and smiled vaguely, as if his thoughts were far away, but just then the door of Sister's room swung open and one of the night nurses came out.

"All ready Father," she smiled at the man on the bench.

Then she caught sight of me.

"'Morning nurse," she said, as we entered the ward where everything seemed to be in chaos, with beds stripped and nurses scurrying to and fro carrying bowls of hot water or balancing heavy screens on their hips, trying not to betray the panic which lay just below the surface of each one's mind at the thought that they might not be ready on time.

"Can you help Mrs. Forrest? Father Hammond has come to give communion to the Catholic patients and she'll probably need a wheelchair: I've set up everything in Sister's room and the others are waiting, so when you've got her in the chair tell Father Hammond they're all ready."

So THAT was who the young man was, the Catholic priest.

I hurried to Mrs. Forrest's bedside: she looked pale and washed out and I wondered what sort of night she had had.

When I wheeled her into Sister's room, with the other four patients shuffling behind me, Father Hammond was already there with the makeshift altar set up before him. I settled them in as told and as I quietly closed the door I could hear the soft murmur of his voice and the quiet responses coming from those seated before him.

Going back into the ward the nurse who had hailed me earlier beckoned me over.

"Come and finish these beds with me. We're late this morning."

"Anything unusual happened in the night?" I enquired, as we swiftly stripped and folded the blankets of the patients who were in the bathroom.

She shook her head.

"No, but having a communion service always holds us up."

I nodded, remembering what it had been like in London for the night nurse in charge of the ward who, on top of everything else, had to turn Sister's room into a small chapel and then return it to its normal state again before she arrived.

She smiled.

"But Father Hammond's such a sweetie, one never minds."

We gave a final pat to the coverlet and passed on to the next bed.

"Mrs. Forrest looks washed out," I said.

Madden looked up at me as we shook the blanket.

"Are you surprised?" she answered drily.

I looked at her blankly.

"I was rather surprised that she needed a wheelchair," I continued. "She said yesterday that she's only got a bad back due to a fall."

I laughed.

"She even said she felt a fraud taking up a bed for such a minor ailment."

Madden looked at me strangely.

"Weren't you here when she was admitted yesterday?" she asked.

"No," I replied. "I arrived just afterwards."

"So you didn't hear Sister give the report?"

"No," I answered, puzzled.

"Then you'd better read her notes," she said laconically as we pummelled and patted the pillows into shape before passing on to the next bed.

I opened my mouth to question her further: she seemed to be a very approachable senior, but at that moment the two patients whose beds we had just finished making sauntered back from the bathroom and all further conversation between us ended.

The outer door opened and the patients who had received communion came back into the ward. One of them was wheeling Mrs. Forrest.

"Go and help her into bed," Madden said, then changed her mind. "No I'll do it, you go and tidy up Sister's room."

I went back through the swing door into Sister's room, where Father Hammond was repacking his little black case. He looked up and smiled again, this time as if he really saw me. As I hurried round putting the room to rights before the dreaded eight chimes rang out, wondering vaguely how we would know the time now that our lives were no longer regulated by Big Ben, I heard myself saying to him:

"How was Mrs. Forrest?"

It was so unexpected: I couldn't understand why I should have this obsession with a patient I had only exchanged a few words with the day before.

He snapped the case shut and straightened up.

"As well as can be expected," he said simply as he walked towards the door. "Thank you for all your help nurse," and he closed it quietly behind him.

It wasn't until that afternoon that I had a chance to look at Mrs. Forrest's notes. The morning had been the usual flurry of ward rounds, dressings to be done, mid-morning hot milk drinks to be served and finally patients to be made comfortable and propped up in bed before lunch arrived. But, although the routine was identical, the atmosphere seemed so much more intimate, more friendly than in the London ward: maybe everything being on a smaller scale helped give the impression of cosiness. Looking through the window as I went from bed to bed with the hot drinks I had seen Morley-Watson changing a plump wriggling baby in the Children's Ward next door: she had looked most uncomfortable and I had giggled at the spectacle.

When we gathered in front of Sister's desk for the afternoon's work list, she looked up kindly at me.

"Do you feel that you are getting to know the patients, nurse?" she asked.

"Well yes Sister," I murmured. "I'm trying."

"By the end of the day you should feel more at home," she went on. "This afternoon I want you to go with Nurse Ogilvie to fold the dressing squares, and get them ready for stoving."

Nurse Ogilvie and I dutifully detached ourselves from the line and walked sedately to the linenry. I was thankful that at least there I could sit down for a short while.

"Are you coming to Scottish dancing tonight?" Ogilvie enquired as we began folding gauze squares.

"I didn't know there was any," I answered.

"Oh yes, every Tuesday evening immediately after supper. It's fun," she said, her hazel eyes twinkling. "Bit short on the male side, but we manage."

"How?" I asked.

I had always enjoyed Scottish dancing but couldn't see that it would be much fun if it were unisex.

"Well, there are the housemen and the RAP comes occasionally when he's free."

"Really?" I said.

The RAP in London had always been way above our heads. I'd never even addressed him directly.

"Oh yes, he's SUPER."

And she giggled.

"Pity he's engaged to a blue striper who's working in the theatre in London. They're getting married next summer when she finishes."

"And the RAS?" I enquired. (The RAS was the Resident Assistant Surgeon.)

"Oh no, not HIM," she grimaced. "He's barely human, works non-stop and never thinks of anything else. Very much on his dignity, though he's quite attractive."

She giggled again.

"The last intake we had, the girl who was here before you mistook him for the porter. She handed him the coal scuttle when he walked into the ward to do his round and told him to hurry and fill it, the stove was almost out. You should have seen his face… AND Sister's."

We both suppressed giggles. This was the sacred hour of the afternoon when the patients were all either sleeping or at least resting after the exertions of the morning, and any peals of hilarity would have echoed throughout the silent ward.

"Who comes then?"

"Oh, anyone who wants to. Mostly US, of course, but there are often students sent here for a time, as well as the housemen, and we manage, though I must say men are rather at a premium down here in the wilds."

She sighed dramatically, then looked up, her hazel eyes twinkling again.

"You should have been here last week," she said. "It was HILARIOUS. One of the housemen was called out just after we started; we were doing Strip the Willow and someone kept slipping the needle back to the beginning just before it ended so the dance went on and on. When Simon came back after having removed an emergency appendix, he just joined the line where he had left it. I think he imagined we had waited for him."

She stifled a laugh behind her hand.

"Living in the wilds DOES have its compensations," she said. "Just imagine that happening up at the hospital."

From my past experience at the hospital I certainly couldn't imagine anything even remotely resembling it happening. Everything there was on such a vast scale; the little intimate touches I was learning about down here simply didn't exist.

"It does seem to be more relaxed and friendly here," I remarked.

Ogilvie folded a square and put it in the tin box before replying.

"Friendly yes," she said at last. "Relaxed no, that's just an illusion. Discipline is just as strict here, but because everything is smaller and cosier we don't tend to notice it so much."

She looked across at me as she shut the lid of the gauze box and reached for another.

"What do you think of Home Sister?" she enquired.

"Quite a character," I answered.

"She certainly is. Got a heart of gold but very changeable. I suppose it's the Irish in her, she can blow up at the drop of a hat. The other week she banned us all from Scottish dancing for something we'd done which the day before she'd probably have laughed her head off about. Oh well," she sighed dramatically, then looked up, her hazel eyes twinkling again, "theirs not to reason why, theirs but to do or die."

The word 'die' suddenly pulled me up with a jerk. Mrs. Forrest's face floated before me and suddenly all joy evaporated from the mild autumn afternoon, all anticipation of the evening's Scottish dancing suddenly waned. I took a deep breath, not quite knowing how to begin.

"Ogilvie," I said hesitantly.

She looked up enquiringly.

"I suppose you've read all the patients' notes?"

"Oh yes," she answered. "Why?"

"I haven't had much time to get to know them yet, though faces are beginning to become familiar."

"It does take a day or so."

"It's Mrs. Forrest," I began. "When I arrived yesterday Sister asked me to make her a cup of tea and then I wheeled her to communion this morning and somehow, I know it's silly, but I can't get her out of my mind. Madden wasn't very expansive when I asked about her but it was difficult, the patients were coming and going, and she suggested I read her notes."

I took a deep breath, almost dreading what might be coming.

"So far I haven't had a chance," I ended.

Ogilvie's eyes clouded over.

"A sad case," she said. "But there are so many in the ward."

"What IS the matter with her?" I pursued. "She told me she had hurt her back being jerked in a taxi. It didn't sound very dramatic to me."

"Oh, that's the story," Ogilvie replied, mechanically folding the gauze into squares and placing them in the box ready for sterilisation. "Unfortunately, the fall flared up a latent cancer which has just shot through her whole body. She hasn't got much more than a month to live; that's why London sent her down here when they discovered what it was. Her home's quite near and it will make it easier for her family to visit her."

The square I was folding fell to the floor as I gazed at my companion in stunned silence.

"Oh NO," I whispered.

Ogilvie looked up at me in surprise. "'Fraid so," she said without undue emotion.

I looked down at the floor, remembering. So that awful premonition, that dreadful wave of sadness which had swept over me when I stood by Mrs. Forrest's bedside the previous evening had been justified.

"Where were you before?" Ogilvie enquired.

"Men's Surgical," I answered, my eyes riveted on the piece of gauze lying at my feet.

She paused and looked across at me.

"You must have come across cases like this?" she asked gently.

I nodded.

"Then why are you so affected?"

I shook my head, bewildered by my own emotion.

"I don't know," I replied. "It's just so sad."

"It's ALWAYS sad," she said softly. "Sometimes it's difficult not to get hardened when one sees so much suffering."

She sighed.

"And what can one do?"

"I don't know," I replied. "Nothing I suppose."

Ogilvie reached for another piece of gauze.

"Mrs. Forrest's is a particularly sad case," she continued, "but there are at least four more in the ward at the moment. Three of them are in their sixties but Mrs. Lind – she's the pretty blond in the end bed on the other side – isn't forty yet. One feels so helpless."

"Does she know?" I enquired.

"Who? Mrs. Forrest?"

I nodded.

"No," Ogilvie answered, "she doesn't, but her husband does and he doesn't want her to be told."

She shrugged.

"One can only respect the family's wishes," she said.

"Would YOU wish to know?" I enquired.

Ogilvie paused and sat for a moment in thoughtful silence.

"Yes," she said, "I think I would, especially if I were married. It's a terrible strain on the one who does know, keeping up the pretence."

She pushed the full box of squares aside and reached for another.

"Mrs. Lind knows," she went on, "and it makes such a difference. One can talk to her and she and her husband can talk openly together... and cry together. Just watch them when he comes to see her, it's heartbreaking but there's something beautiful about it too."

She shrugged.

"But then they both have a very deep Christian faith and it does seem to make a difference."

"You mean it makes it easier for them to accept?" I enquired.

Ogilvie pursed her lips and shook her head.

"Not EASIER, no I wouldn't say that. They are both

absolutely shattered by what has happened, but in spite of everything they have this hope."

We sat in silence for a few minutes mechanically folding pieces of gauze into squares.

"She told me that she knows it's only a temporary parting," Ogilvie went on at last. "A painful parting, but one day they will be together again in heaven. It's amazing, isn't it? She has been able to ACCEPT what is happening – not without tears and questions, but she says she believes that God is in control, that He has a plan for her life and for her husband. She has just put him and her children – she has a girl of eighteen and a boy of sixteen – into God's hands."

Ogilvie shook her head unbelievingly and we neither of us spoke for a few minutes: each, I think, bewildered by Mrs. Lind's reactions and trying, without much success, to understand.

"She was very depressed when she first knew because it was so unexpected, just like Mrs. Forrest's," Ogilvie went on thoughtfully, "but now she says she and her family have prayed through the whole situation and ..."

She stopped abruptly and looked at the blank wall in front of her, then shrugged and finished her sentence.

"Well, you can't deny it, can you? Now she has found this wonderful serenity."

She half turned on her high stool and looked at me.

"It's amazing, isn't it? Can you understand it?"

I shook my head. I couldn't think of anything to say.

Ogilvie looked down at the gauze in her hands and bit her lip.

"She's going home on Saturday," she said softly, "because she wants to spend whatever time is left to her with her family."

She sighed and lapsed again into silence. My mind went back to that Sunday evening in Jane's room when we had talked at such length about the mystery of suffering, and I wondered if I wasn't perhaps at this moment just one more step higher on the ladder which would lead me to understanding. Then I remembered my conversation with Mrs. Forrest the evening before and pain and anger at the injustice of it all boiled up inside me.

"Mrs. Forrest had got a little baby," I said. "She told me she wants to be home for his first birthday in two weeks' time."

Ogilvie looked up and grimaced.

"Don't think there's much hope of THAT," she said.

"But if Mrs. Lind can go home?"

"Mrs. Lind has refused radiation treatment which could prolong her life," Ogilvie said quietly.

I looked at her in surprise.

"She knows what the side effects are," Ogilvie continued, "the awful sickness and exhaustion patients undergoing radiation feel after every session. She says she wants to spend what time is left enjoying her family, not feeling ghastly and upsetting them. I suppose she's got a point."

"I'd have thought she'd have wanted to live as long as possible, just to be with them," I burst out.

"I suppose it all depends on how you look on death," Ogilvie said reflectively. "Mrs. Lind is not afraid, and that makes all the difference: she can talk about it with her husband and children. They cry together as well, but she told me for them death isn't final; she says it's the beginning of life not the end, just like going from one room to another."

She put down the gauze she was folding and looked directly at me.

"Must be wonderful to have such a faith," she ended. "Such certainty that there IS life after death."

"Mrs. Forrest went to mass in Sister's room this morning," I ventured, "so perhaps she has this special faith."

Ogilvie pursed her lips.

"If she had, I don't think the truth would have been kept from her: so she's a Catholic is she? I'm SO glad, she'll have that lovely Father Hammond to help her."

"Is Mrs. Lind a Catholic?" I enquired.

"No she's not, though she does often talk to Father Hammond when he comes in to see his patients. But then they all talk to him, he's SUCH a poppet and unfortunately the resident chaplain down here isn't much help. He's a nice enough chap but a bit ineffective. He doesn't seem to know what to say to the patients who are really distressed. When we ask the Protestant patients who are very ill if they would like to see him, they dive under the bedclothes in a panic."

Her eyes twinkled.

"I think they imagine a visit from him will finish them off. Trouble is, he hasn't really got the manner for the job, he just doesn't click with the patients: he'd do better in a genteel country parish, organising church bazaars and drinking tea with old ladies."

"But they talk to Father Hammond?" I enquired.

"Oh yes, all of them. Sometimes the non-Catholics even ask to speak to him when he comes in. Poor man, he's run off his feet doing the two jobs."

She slammed the lid down on the last box of squares and slipped off the high stool, automatically smoothing her apron as she did so.

"There," she said, "that's that. We'd better get back into the ward, it's almost tea-time. If I don't get a chance to talk to you again, see you tonight at Scottish dancing – just put on a pair of gym shoes, no one dresses up. You'll probably meet the chaplain there, he usually comes: skinny chap, all tooth and legs."

I nodded but didn't reply. Somehow the thought of Scottish dancing, which had so pleased me earlier on, had become distasteful. I felt I just wanted to go away and be alone.

As we tiptoed back into the ward a nurse was attempting to empty the contents of the coal scuttle noiselessly into the stove and not making a very good job of it. The clatter of black nuggets being gobbled up by leaping flames, together with the gentle hiss coming from the large copper steriliser simmering away in the middle of the ward and sending out a soft mist of steam into the warm silent atmosphere, soothed my tormented thoughts. I felt momentarily secure and reassured by the cosiness, the very ordinariness of it all.

Then I caught sight of Mrs. Lind peacefully dozing, her pretty blond hair falling in soft waves about her pale face, and my heart contracted painfully inside my chest as the question I had been torturing myself with for so long rose menacingly once again into my mind. Why? Why the suffering? Why the unfairness of it all? And I longed for Jane to be in my place. She had found the answers; she would know what to say to the condemned patients with whom we were daily coming in contact. She might not be able to explain everything away but at least she would not feel frozen and helpless as I did.

The women were beginning to stir, rousing themselves from their afternoon stupor. As I passed Mrs. Forrest's bed she smiled at me and I felt a lump rise in my throat as I smiled back. But the comforting clatter of cups coming from the kitchen, announcing that tea would soon be on the way, restored normality and the security of routine to my fraught emotions.

Sister looked up from her desk in the middle of the ward, where she was busily writing, as we walked towards her.

"Go and help with the tea-trolley, nurse," she said to me, "and make sure that there are enough sandwiches, they're one short in the kitchen and they may be rushed for time."

Retracing my steps, through the window I caught another glimpse of Morley-Watson. She was exasperatedly trying to shove a spoonful of red and yellow jelly into a protesting toddler's mouth and, seeing the tight disapproving look on her face, the tension inside me broke and I smiled.

CHAPTER THIRTEEN

The Death Sentence

With the wonderful buoyancy of youth, by the time supper was over I was ready and raring to be off Scottish dancing.

"Don't forget nurses," Home Sister said, looming in the swing door as we all hastily discarded our uniforms and searched for gym shoes, "next week CHOIR practice starts."

"CHOIR practice," I muttered to Ogilvie as we bumped into each other in the main aisle, "what on earth is she talking about?"

"Christmas," she answered laconically.

"But Christmas is YEARS away," I exclaimed.

"Not as far as Gert's concerned," she replied as we bent our heads against the rising wind and rushed across the darkened concrete. "She's not keen on our doing Scottish dancing, the Irish in her I suppose, and if she can put a spoke in the wheel she will. Choir practice is one of them. She always starts everyone preparing for the carol singing round the wards on Christmas Eve MONTHS before we need to. I was down here last year at this time and I know. Actually it's hilarious."

I failed to see how choir practice could be hilarious but, knowing Home Sister, was prepared to believe anything.

"Gert takes it herself," Ogilvie went on, "thumping on that old piano as if it were a Sergeant Major's drum and we all bawl out *Good King Wenceslas* in her own four-part setting."

"Four-part?" I queried. "Do the housemen join in too?"

"Not a hope," Ogilvie laughed as we arrived at the door and rushed in out of the cold. "Gert doesn't approve of any mixing of the sexes, that's why she tries to sabotage Scottish dancing every week. No, she forces the more masculine ones among us to sing bass."

"Good role for Morley-Watson," I said drily.

"Oh Anthea?" Ogilvie enquired. "Do you know her? Yes of course you do, she must be in your set."

"Unfortunately," I answered grimly, "and now the poor kids in the Children's Ward have inherited her."

Ogilvie laughed and flopped down on one of the hard wooden chairs which were arranged like sentinels all around the room. Seeing her in the sudden glare of bright light without her cap hiding a mop of chestnut curls, she was really very pretty.

"But how do YOU know her?" I asked.

"Oh," she replied, "we were at school together. Poor girl isn't much fun but then I don't think her life's much fun either. Her mother ran off with the chauffeur of all people when Anthea was only about six and she's been brought up by a succession of governesses and housekeepers ever since. I don't know whether she really WANTED to take up nursing, I think it was more or less expected of her: her father has a large plate up in Harley Street and old Wellyboots is her godmother."

"Old WELLYBOOTS?" I queried.

"Haven't you met Miss Welly yet? Oh you will, don't worry. You must have seen her around. She got some sort of decoration during the war which enables her to wear peculiar garments, at least I think that's what it was."

Ogilvie giggled.

"Don't know WHICH war," she went on. "Probably with Flo in the Crimea."

She looked at me, her hazel eyes dancing with amusement.

"Goes around in half mourning with a vast grey cape flying out behind. Looks like Zorro."

"But what does she DO?" I interrupted.

"Well," Ogilvie pursed her lips, "she calls herself Matron, but only down here. There's only ONE real Matron and that's Miss Pryce-Jones up at the hospital proper, but old Welly gives herself airs and thinks she is too. She ought to have been pensioned off years ago, she and that decrepit secretary of hers – Miss Plumb."

Ogilvie giggled again.

"I suppose you haven't met her either?" she went on.

I shook my head.

"Quite a pair. They're about a hundred. Don't think Miss Pryce-Jones knows what to do with them: Welly's family have all been part of the hospital hierarchy since Doomsday so nobody really dares to tell her to hop it."

"I must say," she sighed, "we DO seem to collect them. When you think of Gert and Wellyboots it makes you wonder if this place hasn't become the dumping ground for all the weirdos the hospital wants to get rid of."

We both laughed.

"Perhaps when you meet her," Ogilvie went on, suddenly serious, "you'll understand why Anthea is as she is. Since her mum did a bunk old Wellyboots has had quite a hand in her upbringing, probably put a gun to her head and forced her to sign on for the PTS."

Feelings of guilt were slowly creeping under my skin as I remembered how unkind we had all been to poor old Morley-Watson, and I wondered once again how many others were hiding their true selves, covering up past pain by a brusque exterior. Some words which I had been obliged to learn in my Sunday school days, 'Man looks to the outside but Jesus looks at the heart,' came back to my mind. Was I judging on appearances, I wondered? Bunty had said how 'toffee-nosed' they had all thought I was until they got to know me: perhaps I should try to get to know Morley-Watson. But the mere idea was distasteful; she just rubbed me up the wrong way and irritated me intensely every time we came into contact with each other. It wasn't until much later that I learned that 'by ourselves we can do nothing': it is only when we ask Jesus to pour His love into us that we are able to see people in a different light.

But at that moment I was still striving, and failing, in my own strength. I was still trying to find an answer to suffering and the meaning to life through human reasoning: I hadn't yet understood that we never can. It is only when we totally, unconditionally surrender ourselves and our lives to Jesus that we can even begin to fathom the mystery of that nagging question 'why'.

"She seems quite KEEN," I said slowly, as these disturbing thoughts continued to swirl around in my mind.

"Oh, she would be," Ogilvie replied. "She's desperate to please. Her Pa and mine are great buddies and my mother used to invite her to stay sometimes during school holidays because she felt sorry for her. Much to my disgust I'll admit, and I must say I avoided her. She was in the same form as my younger sister so I left them to it, though I don't think Fiona appreciated having her around either."

She looked across at me and smiled.

"Aren't schoolgirls horrible?" she laughed. "Poor old Anthea."

At that moment a young houseman carrying a portable gramophone kicked open the door.

Ogilvie waved in his direction.

"That's Adrian," she said, "he always turns the records over for us: going in for anaesthetics. No, Anthea isn't as bad as all that," she ended, her mind jumping like a grasshopper from one subject to another, "just a born pain in the neck, that's all."

She got up and walked over to where another houseman, with a pile of '78 records in his arms, had joined the first, and began looking through them.

"Simon, can we start with the Gay Gordons?" she asked, weaving in and out in a solo figure of eight, a record clutched lovingly to her bosom.

"Bit difficult with just the four of us," he replied, smiling across at me.

Ogilvie waved to me to come and join them.

"Oh, the others will be here any minute," she said, "unless Gert has found an excuse to punish them and send them to bed without supper."

We all laughed as she continued to pirouette and at that moment the door burst open bringing with it a gust of wind and a swirl of leaves as about a dozen student nurses and a leggy young man with prominent teeth rushed in.

Ogilvie stopped twirling and nudged me.

"That's Archie Heeley-Walker," she whispered, "our heart-throb chaplain."

I giggled. He was anything but a heart-throb.

Donaldson appeared wearing authentic dancing pumps and we all lined up for the Dashing White Sergeant. The exercise, the laughter and the sheer hysteria of racing around to the sound of bagpipes squeaking from the old-fashioned gramophone blew away the remaining cobwebs from my mind and I began to see why Ogilvie felt that life in the wilds had its compensations. This feeling was reinforced when in the midst of the general pandemonium, instead of Urquhart and Donaldson who, judging by their names, should have known better, dancing through the arch of joined hands on either side of Adrian, something went wrong and Ogilvie appeared triumphantly leading Simon and Heeley-Walker.

We all collapsed in more hopeless giggles and fell upon the bottles of lemonade, the only liquid sustenance Miss Welly agreed to provide.

The next morning I went on duty with a lighter step, the soothing effect of routine already beginning to have its effect and my spirits considerably raised when I saw Mrs. Forrest sitting up in bed wearing a pretty pink satin bedjacket which seemed to reflect onto her cheeks, infusing them with colour. She appeared to enjoy her breakfast and I took heart, thinking that perhaps Ogilvie had been wrong, perhaps London had made a wrong diagnosis, perhaps everybody had been wrong after all, and she really only had a bad pain in her back and would get better with time and rest.

It was Wednesday, visiting afternoon, and as I went about my duties I saw Mrs. Lind out of the corner of my eye. She was in deep conversation with a woman whom I took to be her mother. She must know, I thought. How can they be so calm, talking as if nothing were wrong? As I passed her bed she beckoned me over.

"Nurse," she said, with a very sweet smile, "could you put these flowers in water for me?"

And she handed me a variegated autumn posy.

"They come from my garden," she confided. "My

daughter picked them before she went to school this morning so that they would be fresh. Aren't they lovely?"

I buried my face in the blooms because for the moment I couldn't speak, it was all too poignant.

"Lovely," I echoed and quickly turned away.

As I walked back into the ward with the vase in my hand the man I had noticed at Mrs. Forrest's bedside the day I arrived walked in behind me. I turned and smiled at him. He smiled back absently: his face looked tired and drawn and my heart went out to him. What was he feeling? What thoughts were going through his mind: how was he coping with this death sentence which had been passed on his wife, a death sentence of which she appeared to be blissfully unaware? How could he bear such a burden alone? And I felt then that perhaps Mrs. Lind was right, or that her husband had been right to tell her, so that they could share the precious time which was left to them; share it and not waste it in the way people so often do when they imagine that their whole lifetime lies ahead.

I placed the sweet smelling bouquet on Mrs. Lind's bedside locker and as I did so the thought came to me that perhaps Mrs. Forrest and Mrs. Lind's cases were not really any different from any of our destinies. They hadn't thought they would die before reaching half of their expected life span and yet did I know, could I say with any certainty that I would attain that allotted span? Did I even know whether I would be here tomorrow? As the thought struck me, I shivered and longed for someone to talk to, someone who could give me the answers. I had caught a glimpse of the truth that evening in Jane's room and then it had elusively disappeared and I wondered where on earth I could go to find it again.

If ONLY Jane were here. Even if she didn't have the answers, she would have words of comfort and peace. And, suddenly, I felt angry with Archie Heeley-Walker. He was supposed to be a man of God: he should be able to supply the answers. Yet apparently he couldn't, he'd failed miserably with all these people who were desperately seeking for some reassurance that life was not pointless, some promise that death was not the end.

Looking up, through the swing door I caught a glimpse of a now familiar figure in a dark suit and clerical collar talking to Sister. As they moved into her room and closed the door, it was almost as if a light dawned in my brain and a torrent of release poured through me.

Father Hammond. Perhaps he could help me.

And then my spirits sank to zero again.

I was a Protestant and he was a Catholic. How could a Catholic priest possibly help someone who had been brought up in what to him must be a heretical church? And yet, Ogilvie had said that he and Mrs. Lind often had long conversations and that the non-Catholic patients were always pleased to have him come and sit by their bedsides and discuss their problems.

But I wasn't a patient: I was a nurse.

"Nurse," Mrs. Forrest called, as I passed her bed. "Come and look. My husband has just brought me in some photos of my little boy taken only last week."

And she eagerly leafed through the packet as I stood by her bed and made admiring remarks.

"Oh, how he's CHANGED," she exclaimed delightedly; "he's not a baby any more, he's a REAL BOY."

She looked up at me and her light green eyes were shining.

"I haven't seen him for nearly a month," she said. "It's amazing how quickly they change at that age."

She turned to her husband.

"I don't suppose you notice it darling, but to me it's incredible how grown up Jonathan's become."

Her husband smiled and said nothing.

"I really MUST be home for his first birthday," she went on, taking her husband's hand. "I never thought when I went in for those tests it would take so much time. Perhaps you could see the doctor and find out just how much longer they expect to keep me here?"

As I handed him back the photographs our eyes met, and he turned away.

"I'll make an appointment," he said soothingly, squeezing her hand.

But the bell for the end of visiting time sounded and he got up abruptly, I think almost with relief, his shoulders bowed under the weight of the burden he was carrying.

As the visitors streamed towards the door, Mrs. Forrest settled contentedly back on her pillows and, opening the envelope, began to look through the photographs once again.

CHAPTER FOURTEEN

Crossing the Great Divide

The following Saturday morning Sister told me to fetch Mrs. Lind's clothes and see if she needed any help in dressing: her husband was coming to take her home.

As she sat by her bed waiting, the peacock blue suit hanging baggily on her rapidly wasting figure, she looked the picture of happiness.

"You'll be orl rite now dearie," the old lady in the next bed said, "you're goin' 'ome."

Mrs. Lind smiled sweetly.

"I'm so looking forward to it," she answered. "It will be lovely to be with John and the children and be a family again, instead of only seeing them on visiting days."

"You're lucky you are," Doris sniffed. "I'm 'ere till Christmas at least."

I winked conspiratorially at Mrs. Lind as I passed by. Doris was a regular 'winter resident'. She lived in a tiny damp tumbledown cottage not far from the hospital gate and as soon as the weather began to get cold she was always brought in 'suffering' from G.O.K., as it was called by whichever houseman admitted her that year. She was very proud of the diagnosis: "Got G.O.K. again dearie," she used to say confidentially, "but they're treating me." We looked suitably impressed and played her game, never letting on that G.O.K. stood for 'God only knows'. There was nothing physically wrong with Doris, nothing that necessitated hospital treatment that is; she was merely suffering from loneliness, deprivation and hopelessness and the only way she could face the winter was by being admitted to the hospital, or 'orspital' as she called it, where she was kept warm and fed and generally fussed over until spring came around again.

Sometimes, if it turned mild in the New Year – she was never denied her Christmas festivities in hospital – Sister would suggest that perhaps the symptoms had subsided and she could go home. But Doris always promptly had another 'attack', was 'took bad' as she said and, unless there was a real emergency and a desperate shortage of beds, was allowed to stay.

While Mrs. Lind sat waiting, patiently listening to Doris's recital of her ailments, I wondered whether SHE would still be with her family at Christmas and suddenly all the anguish I had felt when I first arrived and gave Mrs. Forrest that cup of tea washed over me again. Looking up, I saw Father Hammond striding down the ward.

"'Lo Farva," Doris chirped, "'ow ya doin'?"

"Hallo Doris," he said warmly, "I'll come and have a chat with you in a minute, I just want to see Mrs. Lind before she goes home."

And he drew up a chair by her bed.

I longed to eavesdrop, to hear what it was they were saying. It didn't appear to be a morbid conversation; he was leaning towards her speaking earnestly, but she was smiling and once I saw her reach out and pat his hand. As he got up to go, her husband and two children came in to the ward and Mrs. Lind stood up excitedly, placing a hand on Father Hammond's arm.

"I'm SO glad they've arrived before you left," she said delightedly. "I just want you to meet the most wonderful family in the world."

And they all laughed.

Her husband bent down and kissed her.

"All ready?" he asked tenderly.

"All ready," she smiled back up at him.

As her son picked up her suitcase and her husband gently took her arm, I fled to the sluice, the tears which had long been held back ready to spill and cascade in a torrent down my cheeks. And wiping my eyes once again on the rough roller towel, through the window I saw the most wonderful family in the world walk out into the autumn sunshine. Sister was with them and, as they stopped to bid her goodbye, Mrs. Lind squeezed her arm and smiled confidently at her then, one hand tucked happily under her husband's arm and the other resting lightly on her daughter's, turned and walked bravely and joyfully away into the future, knowing full well what it would hold.

I went back into the ward and as I stopped to remove the mid-morning cocoa cup which had been left on Mrs. Forrest's locker, she looked up at me.

"Lovely to see people leave, isn't it, nurse?"

I nodded.

"And she looks so WELL."

Her eyes shone brightly up at me.

"Perhaps next week it will be MY turn."

I smiled and moved away. Father Hammond was now sitting with Doris listening to a long diatribe of her various ailments. I marvelled at the patience of the man, and once again wondered what had passed between him and Mrs. Lind in those few minutes before she left. They both knew that she was going home to die and yet they had been able to talk together, unemotionally and without apparent sadness. And although they came from different denominations, they appeared to be in tune and to understand each other.

Ogilvie's words in the linenry on that first afternoon came back to me:

"But Mrs. Lind and her husband have a deep Christian faith. They say that they believe that God is in control and that He has a plan for their lives: that this is only a temporary parting and they will meet again in heaven. And, believing that, she has been able to put herself and her family in God's hands, knowing that He will look after them."

I shook my head in disbelief but I couldn't get away from the fascination I felt towards a God who cares, a God who really DOES have a plan for our lives. Jane had confirmed this to me and I had even felt it myself that morning in the hospital chapel. And yet, in spite of everything, I still could not accept or even begin to understand why Mrs. Lind's life should be cut off halfway through, why the suffering.

Then Jane's words came back to me:

"Suffering is a part of life, no one escapes it; it all depends on what we do with it."

I realised that both she and Mrs. Lind were on the same track, the right track. They had both suffered deeply, but although they didn't know the answer to the question 'why' they had accepted their experience as a part of life and decided not to waste it but to turn it into something positive. And I heard Jane's voice once again saying:

"I don't know all the answers but I know Jesus, and for the moment that is all I need."

Mrs. Lind also knew Jesus, and it seemed that He was all she and her family needed at this traumatic time in their lives. And suddenly that same feeling of envy I had felt when I knew that Jane had something which seemed to be eluding me, to be beyond my grasp, now crept over me again, and to my astonishment, I realised that I was almost envying Mrs. Lind!

Father Hammond had managed to escape from Doris's clutches and was now sitting playing dominoes with a young girl of twelve doomed for the next few months to lie flat on her back with a heart complication resulting from rheumatic fever. Kathleen was Irish and I knew she was a Catholic. She was a sweet uncomplaining girl, one of eight children, and she didn't have many visitors. Her family lived in the East End of London near the docks, where her father worked as a casual labourer, so trips to the hospital were a rare treat for them.

She had been in the ward for over a month now, having been sent down from the main hospital as a long-term patient, and the priest had taken the place of her family. He visited her as often as he could and brought little treats from his own meagre rations to tempt her.

As I went about my work, I began to wonder what had prompted him to become a priest, to give up what appeared to me to be everything and spend his time with the sick, the dying and those with seemingly unsolvable problems. And I wondered if it was this faith which, up till a few months ago, I had thought I had but now realised that I didn't have, at least not in the same way as he and Jane and Mrs. Lind.

Suddenly I almost collided with a tall thin figure in a black cassock. It was Archie Heeley-Walker. He smiled vaguely – I don't think he recognised me from Tuesday evening's jigging – and started to walk down the ward, stopping at the foot of each bed to enquire after the patient's health but never going any nearer, almost as though he were afraid of having any personal contact with the women lying there in front of him.

As he approached Kathleen's bed, Father Hammond clasped his hand to his head in mock despair.

"You've beaten me AGAIN Kathleen," he cried.

He swept the dominoes up into the box then wagged a finger sternly at her.

"But I'll get you next time," he threatened.

She laughed delightedly as he got up and went towards the chaplain: the two men stood chatting amiably together for a few minutes then Heeley-Walker swept out of the ward, the tassles of his cassock swinging rhythmically back and forth behind him.

Father Hammond walked over to Mrs. Forrest's bed and sat down. I could see him nodding his head and smiling.

"I've just told nurse," she said to him as I picked up her bed chart to check her fluid intake, "that perhaps next week it will be my turn to go home."

He looked at her gravely but didn't reply and I wondered why he didn't say something; why he didn't warn her, give her an inkling of the truth. Then I realised that whatever he felt, whatever he longed to say, he was obliged to respect her husband's wishes. James Forrest had made it abundantly clear that under no circumstances was his wife to be told and I queried whether he was right. I felt sure that Father Hammond could have helped Mrs. Forrest, could have comforted her: she was an intelligent woman, perhaps she already half guessed the truth. And then it struck me that perhaps the only way her husband could cope with his own grief was by keeping her in ignorance and thereby pretending that everything was going to be all right, that this terrible sentence had not been passed on his wife.

But Mrs. Forrest's turn to leave the ward to go home never came and, far from being there for her little boy's first birthday, she was never to hold him in her arms or cuddle or play with him again. His birthday came and went and his grandmother brought in a large piece of cake for all of us but, by then, Mrs. Forrest was sinking and not able to eat very much, although she roused herself to look at the pile of birthday cards her baby had received. On the following Sunday afternoon we raised her gently on her pillows and her husband held their little son up at the window outside so that she could see him.

She smiled and waved weakly and her child smiled back automatically; he had not seen his mother for several weeks and his large blue eyes did not show any immediate sign of recognition. His father took his little gloved hand and waved it for him, pointing to the wasted figure lying propped in the bed and saying something to the child but, apart from mechanically waving, he didn't respond and, after a few minutes, wriggled round and buried his face in his father's broad shoulder.

Sister motioned to James Forrest with her head and he waved, blew a kiss to his wife then turned away as she fell back onto her pillows exhausted. She did not say anything; she showed no emotion but for the rest of the afternoon she was very quiet, lying with her eyes fixed on the window where her child had been almost as if she knew that this was the last time that she would ever see him.

Father Hammond came with her husband the following Saturday evening to give her extreme unction and, on the Sunday morning, just as we were gathering for the ward service, screens were put around Mrs. Forrest's bed and we knew that the end was not far away.

"Start the service without me," Sister whispered to Madden. "I MUST get hold of Mr. Forrest. I rang earlier but there was no reply from his home. I'll try his mother-in-law's number, he might just be there."

She glanced across at the closed screens behind which Ogilvie was sitting with the dying patient.

"I don't think she can last much longer."

The rest of us clustered around the piano, business as usual, though there was a subdued hush in the ward and I don't think any of us felt much like singing. Although nothing had been said, the other patients knew that Mrs. Forrest was dying and all, I think, were grateful for the security, the humdrum of routine, with life in the ward continuing as if nothing were happening.

And I think we were too, though I was relieved that the hymns Sister had chosen were not the rousing ones we had often sung so lustily in Men's Surgical. *Praise my Soul the King of Heaven* and *Onward Christian Soldiers* would probably have choked us at that moment.

Madden announced the first hymn and as we all bravely broke into *The King of Love my Shepherd is* I happened to glance across at Doris and saw tears streaming down her lined cheeks. Our singing was rather hoarse too but we managed it; the service continued and I think that when it was over, we all felt better because it had happened.

Sister came back into the ward as we were collecting up the hymn books.

"I can't get hold of Mr. Forrest," I heard her say in an undertone to Madden "No one seems to know where he is."

"I'll keep trying Sister," Madden replied.

Sister hesitated for a moment.

"No," she said, "I won't go off duty this morning, I'll just keep ringing round. I'll be in my room if you need me."

Sister had been on duty almost non-stop since eight o'clock the previous Monday morning as it had been a very busy week and the Charge Nurse had had an attack of tonsillitis and been confined to the Sick Wing. She looked very tired and she needed those few hours' relaxation away from the cares of the ward, but Madden knew that it was no use her telling her so.

Towards the end of the morning I was sent to relieve Ogilvie so that she could go to early lunch. As I tiptoed behind the screens and sat down beside the still figure in the bed her lips moved imperceptibly, but even though I bent down close to her face I could not catch what she was trying to say.

Sister had still not managed to locate her husband and so we were taking it in turns to sit with Mrs. Forrest. When I was in training no patient was ever left to face death alone and, should no relative or friend be present at their bedside, one of the nurses on the ward was always sent to sit with them until that moment when they crossed the great divide and passed from this world into the next. It was a beautiful rule and I know that it brought comfort to many a grieving relative to learn that their loved one had not died alone, had not gone through this great experience without someone they knew beside them to hold their hand and ease their passing. It also helped them, as I later discovered, to be able to talk to the nurse who had seen the final chapter of their loved one's life come to a close, to know just what had happened in those last few seconds before the veil had come down and the door had closed for ever.

As I sat there in an uncanny silence – it seemed that the only sound in the ward that grey overcast morning was the gentle hiss of steam escaping from the large brass steriliser – Sister silently drew the screen a little to one side and bent to feel Mrs. Forrest's almost imperceptible pulse. She straightened up and looked down at her for a few seconds, deep compassion in her clear grey eyes.

"Go and have lunch nurse," she said softly. "I'll take over."

The last thing I wanted was lunch but, once again, the security of routine engulfed me. Life must go on and already the smell of roast lamb was seeping through the screens as the trolley with the patients' Sunday dinner was being wheeled round.

I tiptoed out and went to the linenry to collect my cloak. It was a blustery day with a slight drizzle falling and yet it was good to be out in the open, out in the clean fresh air after the tension and emotion of the morning.

I had grown close to Mrs. Forrest during the past weeks. She was not so much older than I and was a cultured woman with a lively interest in everything, an artist who had previously worked for a well-known weekly magazine. We had so often chatted together whilst I washed her or made her bed or, in the later stages, helped her to swallow the tiny portions of liquid nourishment which was all that she could manage, and had discovered that we had a lot in common. And although I had known her prognosis from the beginning, when one is fond of someone, one always imagines that they are immortal, as one imagines oneself to be. Death is for others, never for ourselves or those we love. It was a shock now to be faced with the reality and, walking briskly along through the lines of huts, I wondered whether I would ever get used to it, ever become hardened by the suffering which now seemed to be my daily portion.

As these thoughts went through my head, my mind went back to Sister, so different from the one I had worked under in London and yet so similar in her total devotion to the patients in her care. I knew that my former Sister would have done just what my present Sister was now doing, given up her precious free time to sit with someone whose life was slowly ebbing away. And, realising this, I felt that I was drawing slowly nearer to that truth which I was so earnestly seeking: the meaning to life, the reason for it all. I knew that there had to be a reason, there had to be an unseen hand in all this. There had to be more then just this earthly passage through life, this brief span, or else where was the justice, what possible explanation could there be for the tragedy being enacted in the ward at this very moment? And once again from the depths of my childhood memory I recalled these words:

'Whoever wants to save his life will lose it, but whoever loses his life will find it. What good will it be for a man if he gains the whole world, yet forfeits his soul?'

They were just a few verses from the Bible which I had been obliged to learn by heart at school, but now that parrot learning was bearing fruit as those words ran through my head. I had no idea what book they came from, whether from the Old Testament or the New, I simply remembered them as being Bible passages and they comforted me.

Then other words floated into my mind:

'For now we see through a glass darkly but then we shall see face to face.'

And I clearly remembered that Monday morning in

school when I had had them hammered into me: I must have been about eight years old at the time and they had meant nothing. All that the 'glass darkly' had conjured up in my mind was the cool dim hall of my great-aunt Jessica's house where a large mirror was hanging, and there one did indeed see through it darkly, so darkly in fact that I had once terrified myself when a set of antlers fixed on the opposite wall had suddenly loomed up out of the gloom behind me as I had stood preening myself in the mirror. I had run screaming in terror, convinced that the devil, who was a very real presence in my youth, a nasty man with a forked tail and horns not unlike the stag's antlers, was creeping up to grab me.

But now the meaning gradually began to disengage itself from the mists of the past. I saw that here on earth we do indeed see through a glass darkly, a glass through which the light is filtered, and it is only when we pass on to the other side that we shall see the light and meet Him who is the light face to face.

I thought once again of Mrs. Forrest, that still, almost lifeless figure whose shallow breathing scarcely moved the bedclothes and I wondered whether, at this moment, she was still this side of the glass seeing through it darkly or whether she had already passed through it to the other side into the light.

And as this thought came to me, it seemed that an immense light surrounded me. The tension and gloom which had so oppressed me during the morning suddenly lifted and I realised, on entering the clatter and chatter of the dining hut, that I was hungry after all.

CHAPTER FIFTEEN

Facing Suffering – and Beyond

That impression of intense light, that 'something' which I had experienced on my way to lunch, had so infused me that I walked cheerfully back into the ward afterwards, humming a tune under my breath. As I entered Mr. Forrest brushed past me and flung out through the swing door. He didn't appear to see me. Sister came noiselessly from behind the green screen and gently pulled it to.

I looked across at Ogilvie: imperceptibly she nodded and I knew that it was all over. Mrs. Forrest had been with us just four weeks and six days.

Sister walked over to her desk and began sorting through papers.

"You and Nurse Greville tidy the beds," she said as I stood in front of her, "and see that the patients are comfortable, the visitors will be here in half an hour."

And, without showing any undue emotion, she sat down at her desk and began writing.

I marvelled at her composure. Mine was shattered.

I had not really come across death before. Patients had died in my former ward but the first had been an elderly man who had gone in the night when I was not there, followed by two others who had complications after surgery: but they had both died on my day off and, although other patients had had exploratory surgery and been discharged with heavy hearts knowing that there was nothing that medical science could do for them, somehow it had not hit me in the way Mrs. Forrest's death had done.

I had known her, grown fond of her, I had met her mother and her husband, talked with them, heard amusing stories about her baby's antics, been part of their life, and now I felt that I was also part of their grief.

As we walked to the other end of the ward to begin the inevitable bed tidying I whispered to Greville:

"What time did she die?"

"Oh, just after you went to lunch," she whispered back.

"Had Sister managed to get hold of her husband?"

"Yes, but he arrived a few minutes too late."

We each grabbed a screen and wedged it firmly on our hips, preparatory to giving out the bedpans.

"How was he?" I whispered, as we marched together to the first bed.

"Pretty shattered: they always are when they're not there. He was on his way to his mother-in-law's to pick up his little boy when Sister first rang his home, then when she got on to the mother-in-law he'd just left to take him out for a walk and no one knew exactly where they'd gone. It was only when they arrived back that he got the message and he dashed straight over. But it was just too late."

"Poor man," I breathed, as we put the screens up round Doris's bed.

Greville didn't say anything and I glanced across at the closed screens behind which up till an hour ago, Mrs. Forrest had still been shallowly breathing. It seemed incredible that now, although outwardly everything was the same, that breath had gone out of her body, her spirit had passed on and, for her and for her husband, nothing would ever be the same again. And while I knew that a new and sadder life was now beginning for her husband and little son, I had the firm conviction that a new and better life had already begun for her.

The screens remained round the lifeless form in the bed the whole afternoon. Visitors came and went and the sounds of animation mounted as friends and relatives greeted each other, flowers were unwrapped and paper bags rustling with goodies were squeezed into lockers. We were kept busy supplying vases and plates and bowls for the fruit and cakes and biscuits and generally making ourselves useful, whilst trying to be as unobtrusive as possible as families were once again briefly reunited.

Sunday and Wednesday afternoons were always a time of

hiatus in the afternoon routine when we felt as if we were standing in the wings, waiting for our turn to go back on the stage which had temporarily been taken over by other actors. But finally, the bell signalling the end of visiting time rang, the crowd dispersed and peace returned to the ward.

Tea, that British panacea for all ills, that solution to all problems, that comfort in the midst of the worst storm, was always immediately served upon the heels of the departing visitors and on Sundays there was cake, a special treat, to help raise the spirits of those facing the inevitable emptiness of long days stretching ahead without seeing their loved ones.

The short November afternoon drew to a close and darkness was falling when a porter discreetly arrived in the ward pushing an empty trolley.

Sister beckoned to me.

"Go with the porter, nurse," she said quietly. "He's come to take Mrs. Forrest to the mortuary."

I suddenly felt as though I had been kicked in the ribs and all breath had been jerked out of my body. I opened my mouth, but no words came. I didn't know what to say, though I knew that no remark was expected of me and that it was not in my power to refuse, but at that moment I felt I couldn't do it. I couldn't go to the mortuary with that lifeless form who had once been like an old friend.

But Sister's eyes had dropped back to the notes in front of her. She picked up her pen and I knew that there was no excuse possible.

Tiptoeing behind the screen I helped the porter lift what remained of Mrs. Forrest onto the trolley and drew the sheet up over her waxen face. Almost without anyone noticing, we slipped out through the swing doors and into the now dark rain-lashed precincts.

As I walked slowly beside him along the concrete path, past the mass of huts, out beyond the hospital proper towards the mortuary, he looked up at me and I tried to smile. But my face appeared to be frozen. He was an elderly man and he seemed to read my thoughts. Suddenly he stopped. We were now away from all the huts, in the middle of the no-man's land which separated the main buildings from the mortuary, and I looked at him in surprise, hugging my cloak around me for protection against the driving rain and the wind which was now howling eerily around us, whipping my thin linen dress against the back of my legs. The mild damp autumn days had suddenly turned to winter with a vengeance, with the promise of worse to come.

"You go back to the ward, nurse," he said kindly. "I can manage on me own."

"But Sister…" I began.

"She needn't know," he answered. "Just walk back slowly, I'll catch you up: she'll never know you haven't come all the way with me. You look done in."

I hesitated, then I nodded to him gratefully. Glancing down once again at the trolley and the stiff outline underneath the sheet, I clutched my cloak more tightly round me and, holding on to my cap with my other hand, headed back into the wind towards the comfort and security of the beckoning lights.

When I walked back into the ward, Sister came towards me.

"You can help me with the beds, nurse," she said. "We'll start by making up number one."

Number one had been Mrs. Forrest's bed.

I followed her behind the still closed screens. The faint pungent smell of lysol clung to the freshly disinfected bedframe, but the bed was stripped and bare. Even the mattress had gone, sent to be stoved, and another one and fresh blankets and linen were already there, waiting to be made up for the next patient. The locker on which had so recently stood the photo of a chubby little boy with soft blond hair was empty, its disinfected interior gaping open. All her personal effects had been removed and even the faint lingering scent of her matching soap and talcum powder which had clung round the bed for the past few weeks had disappeared: nothing was now left to remind us of the woman who until that afternoon had been an integral part of our everyday life.

Sister briskly shook out the clean undersheet and swiftly,

efficiently, impersonally and silently, as if nothing had happened, we began to make the bed. But as we tucked the last blanket into place I looked across at that empty locker and a lump rose in my throat. Perhaps a gulp escaped me, I can't remember. But Sister suddenly dropped the crisp white counterpane with the cross worked down the centre onto the bed and stood facing me.

"Nurse," she said sternly, "pull yourself together."

I looked at her in amazement, unaware that I had betrayed any emotion.

"I know how you feel," she went on quietly, the sharp edge now gone from her voice. "We were all fond of Mrs. Forrest and we all feel as you do: if we didn't we wouldn't be much use as nurses. But, having said that, you cannot let what you feel dictate the way you behave. We have done all we can for Mrs. Forrest. Now we can do no more for her BUT there are twenty-nine other patients out there who need you, and the way you look is going to affect the way they feel."

She paused and looked at me kindly.

"They are upset too, you know," she went on, "and WE are responsible for them. If you go out there wearing that long face they will all be affected. Now, get a grip on yourself, smile and REMEMBER, those who are left NEED you."

And without another word she took the counterpane, deftly smoothed it into position on the bed and, motioning to me to take the other screen, walked across the ward with hers balanced securely on her hip.

Following her I realised that what she had said was true. As those screens were removed, the other twenty-nine patients were all watching, waiting for our reactions. And the way we reacted would determine their mood. Seeing us swiftly move on to the next bed, the next job in hand, normality returned after the trauma; they all, inaudibly, breathed a sigh of relief, took their cue from us and settled quietly and I think thankfully down to the evening routine.

* * * * * *

Just as we were going off duty that evening, Sister asked me to make Doris, who was restless, her n'th cup of tea that day, so when I finally left the ward the patients had already settled down to sleep, the night nurses were going quietly about their duties, the day nurses had all left and I walked out alone into the damp windy precincts.

The rain had stopped but the wind was just as strong and, heading into it, I saw Father Hammond walking out of Men's Surgical opposite. I wondered whether he EVER took any time off.

"Good evening nurse," he said pleasantly, and fell into step beside me.

I glanced up at him. Under the glare of the crude lights which bordered the concrete path he looked desperately tired.

"I expect it's been a busy day for you," I ventured.

He smiled and nodded.

"You've heard about Mrs. Forrest?"

"Yes."

"Have you seen her husband?"

"I spent most of the afternoon with him," he said. "He rang me as soon as he got home from the hospital."

"How was he?"

Father Hammond shrugged.

"Shattered," he answered briefly, and we walked on in silence.

"Poor man," I breathed, "and yet he expected it: he knew."

"What we know with our heads doesn't always translate itself to our emotions," he said. "And sometimes it's the most intelligent people, the ones who can work out and rationalise life, who are the most affected when death comes."

I looked up at him enquiringly.

"I don't pretend to be intellectual," I murmured, "but I know I'D be shattered."

Father Hammond looked down at me.

"I think you ARE shattered," he said quietly, and I knew that his piercing slate-blue eyes had looked right through me. "You were fond of Mrs. Forrest weren't you, nurse?"

I nodded.

"Is this your first real taste of death?"

As he said it I was very conscious of my belt, which signified to all who were in the know that I was still in my first year. He knows I'm only a beginner I said to myself, I suppose he thinks I'm being hysterical. And suddenly, inexplicably, I knew that it mattered to me what he thought.

"Oh," I shrugged, "I've come across it before."

"Death is only a horizon," he said quietly, as we walked along between the now dimly lit huts. "Merely the limit of our sight, that's all. We don't lose our loved ones when God takes them home any more than He loses them when He gives them to us for whatever space of time they are on this earth."

He took a deep breath.

"What is His is ours," he went on softly, "if we belong to Him: they merely go on ahead and help Him prepare a place for us when our time comes."

"But Mrs. Forrest had such a SHORT time," I burst out. "A few months ago she was enjoying life and then in five weeks she changed from a healthy happy woman into a skeleton."

The priest passed his hand wearily through his thick dark hair.

"One can live a lifetime in five weeks," he said quietly. "I think Mrs. Forrest did."

"What do you mean?"

"She had a real encounter with Jesus before she died."

There it was again, someone talking about this encounter with Jesus, this encounter which I knew I must have if ever I was to be able to put together the pieces of my life, and find an answer to the questions which were tormenting me.

"But she was a Catholic before she came in," I queried.

Father Hammond smiled indulgently.

"Being a Catholic doesn't mean a person knows JESUS," he said kindly, "any more than being an Anglican or a Baptist or a Methodist does. So many church people just give cerebral assent, they don't open their hearts to our

Saviour: they merely follow the rules of their particular denomination. But Jesus doesn't belong to ANY denomination, He comes to each one of us personally, offering us freedom from man-made rules; whether we accept Him or not depends on us."

We had now reached the end of the concrete path which divided the wards and the lights of the nurses' home were beckoning in the distance.

"I wish I could really understand what you are saying," I murmured.

"You can," he said quietly. "It's very simple: all you have to do is ask Jesus to come into your heart."

I paused and we stood at the parting of the ways, looking at each other under the glaring arc lamps.

"But HOW?" I asked desperately. "Why if it's so easy is Mr. Forrest so shattered? Why can't HE accept?"

"Because he hasn't yet come to the point where he knows that the only answer is a total surrender of himself. He's been brought up a Catholic but he's also a scientist and he wants cut-and-dried answers to everything."

"Don't we all," I muttered.

"Perhaps," he replied. "But we don't find peace until we finally accept that we'll never get them in this life. I just pray that one day James Forrest will come to realise that."

"With your help?" I asked, looking up at him.

"If he wants it," Father Hammond smiled. "But he doesn't need me. We can come to Jesus without any human intervention, that's what's so wonderful; we just have to acknowledge our need, that's all, and HE will come to US."

He looked down at me under the glaring lights and I saw a muscle working in his cheek.

"He meets each person individually," he said quietly, "at the point of their deepest need."

Jane's words echoed through my mind:

"He came to me at the point of my deepest need."

And I began to wonder whether what he had just been telling me was taught in a manual which they had all learned off by heart. But as I stood there with his gaze upon me I knew that however it was learned, I wanted to learn it too.

"And will we then understand everything?" I enquired.

"What do you mean by EVERYTHING?" he smiled.

"Well, all the 'why's.'"

"You'll certainly understand some of them," he answered kindly. "But we're not meant to understand everything, otherwise there'd be no need for faith, would there?"

I looked up at him blankly.

"Faith is the hope, the assurance of things unseen," he said gently. "No one hopes for things he already has."

My mind was boggling, groping in a thick fog.

"There are some things we will only understand when we meet Jesus face to face in heaven," he went on. "I suppose you're wondering why Mrs. Forrest died?"

I nodded.

"I can't answer that one, just as I can't tell you why some apples fall off the tree when they're still green, others fall at the expected time and others stay on until they are all gnarled and dried up. There is no explanation, and it's the same with life."

He passed his hand through his hair again.

"We don't know why some people die young," he continued softly, "and others stay on long after their expected life span; if we did we'd be God. We only know that each one of us is different and special, very special to Him. He chose us for a purpose, for a specific work, and we are all immortal till our life's work is done."

He shrugged.

"With some it's finished early, with others it takes longer."

He sighed.

"And some never even discover what their life's work was supposed to be, because they never meet Him."

"But why did Mrs. Forrest have to die and leave that little baby?" I burst in. "She loved him, she longed to be home with him and yet, in the last two months of her life she only ever saw him through the window of a hospital ward: she couldn't hold him in her arms, she couldn't even give him one last cuddle."

I felt myself near to tears again.

"I don't know," he said quietly. "I only know that Jesus said, 'If a man keeps my word he will never see death'. If we believe that, then death becomes a healing and all we can do is trust; for nothing that happens to us down here can ever alter God's love."

But suddenly his words irritated me. I didn't at that moment want to trust. I wanted an explanation: I wanted to know why.

"It's my own fault," I said tightly, afraid of betraying my feelings, "for getting emotionally involved with a patient. I'll make sure it never happens again."

And I started to turn away, but he put his hand on my arm and restrained me.

"Nurse," he said gently, "if you aren't emotionally involved with a patient you can't really care for them. It's a dilemma which sometimes splits us right down the middle, all of us who have chosen to work in hospitals: we are ALWAYS at risk, never safe or secure, ALWAYS vulnerable. But it doesn't really matter because no one wants to be looked after by someone who is NOT vulnerable."

He suddenly realised that he was standing facing me with his hand still on my arm and he smiled shyly as he dropped it to his side.

"In caring," he went on, "as you've just proved, in allowing yourself to be open and vulnerable to other people's pain and grief then you are deliberately, but perhaps unconsciously, helping to share the burden of this world's pain and sickness and grief. The are those who bear these burdens as they bear joy and satisfaction, not just for themselves, but on behalf of the people they come in contact with."

He paused and I saw that tell-tale muscle, which I had noticed earlier, working in his cheek again.

"Life has become perpetual motion," he said, sadly shaking his head. "People seem to imagine that they have to be 'doing' all the time: sometimes there's nothing we can do except just be there and let them talk about their hurts and their fears – simply love and accept them in that particular situation, however hopeless it may seem."

I stood looking up at him, my irritation gone, my head in a whirl from all he had been saying to me, not understanding, but hungry to know more.

"But WHY is the cost of caring so high?" I eventually cried out.

He didn't answer immediately and I saw the rain, which had started again, spatter his forehead and trickle down his face.

"Because caring is what God does," he said almost inaudibly. "If you lose touch with God, you lose touch with caring."

His eyes, so deep-set yet so piercing in their intensity, seemed to be far away under the crude arc lights.

"If I needed to seek further for an answer," he went on, his voice scarcely above a whisper, "I'd merely look up and see a young man in his early thirties hanging on a cross."

He paused and passed a hand wearily across his face, now glistening with raindrops.

"And I don't have to ask any more," he ended.

We stood there facing each other in silence, and I was afraid to break the spell. Then, suddenly, I saw the lights begin to go out in the nurses' home and looking at my watch I realised that in ten minutes the entire hut would be plunged into darkness.

"Oh," I gasped, wondering why Gert hadn't been stampeding all over the hospital looking for me. "I MUST go, it's almost lights out."

His eyes slowly focused again as he seemed to come back from a very long way away.

"I'm sorry, nurse, I shouldn't have kept you talking."

"Oh no," I said, clutching my cloak more closely round me as the rain began to lash down again with even greater fury, "I'm SO glad you did."

He turned up the collar of his black jacket against the rain. It occurred to me that I had never seen him wearing an overcoat whatever the weather. And I wondered whether he even had one.

"If you want to continue this conversation at any time..." he ventured.

"Oh please," I breathed, ducking my head as I prepared to brace myself into the wind and cross the few feet of open ground which separated us from the nurses' home. "Yes, I WOULD like to but..."

Another light had just been extinguished in the hut and now only the dangling bulb in Sister's room, which I could see glaring through the unclosed curtains, showed the way.

"I REALLY must go, or there'll be trouble."

Father Hammond smiled and, as I ran swiftly through the gale towards the one remaining light, he turned and walked slowly down the concrete path towards the gate.

CHAPTER SIXTEEN

Oh là là, Nosey-Anne

The winter, which had set in early, proved to be desperately cold and unusually severe. The wards and the nurses' home were kept warm and cosy by the hissing coal stoves which had to be constantly poked and stoked, but the stretches of barren ground in between were death traps and we piled layers of woolly jumpers and cardigans on under our cloaks as we battled with the wind which tore across the desolate barren spaces.

On the wards we had an earwig invasion of everything from beds to dressing packs and even so somehow managed to learn about invalid cookery: how to make arrowroot, which nobody ever appeared to eat, and sponge cakes with powdered eggs, to tempt the convalescent appetite. Unfortunately I forgot to put the flour in mine and produced a result that had to be hastily concealed. To cap it all we were severely scolded by Gert for contracting coughs and colds, sore throats and chilblains because they disrupted the Tuesday evening choir practice!

Ogilvie had been right. This was hilarious to say the least. Gert was really quite a talented musician but, like everything else she did, her efforts tended to turn into a first-class farce. I often wished I'd had a tame film producer up my sleeve who could have hidden behind the curtains during our rehearsals. After witnessing our sessions with *A Virgin Most Pure* (sung solo) and *Sing Lullaby*, with Gert in command producing an incredible din thumping on the rickety old piano with one hand, conducting wildly with the other and stamping the foot which wasn't crashing about on the creaking pedals up and down on the floor to beat out the rhythm, he would have produced a comedy worthy of the Marx Brothers.

This weekly entertainment did not exactly replace Scottish dancing which continued without us, as it was only first-year nurses who were expected to parade round the wards on Christmas Eve, candle in one hand, words and music in the other and cloaks turned inside out to reveal the bright red flannel lining, singing sweetly to the long-suffering patients. But although we grumbled at being denied our one highlight of the week, we didn't really mind as Gert's antics more than made up for the reels we were missing.

With all this going on, although I saw and chatted to Father Hammond who was often in and out of the wards, I didn't actually speak to him alone again.

Christmas was always a very busy time for the hospital since everything was done to make it as festive as possible for those patients who were unfortunate enough to be there. Apart from the efforts of the choir, all the decorations were made and put up by the nurses so that on the days running up to Christmas there was much swinging about on ladders and high-pitched shrieking as we wobbled around on rickety steps hanging up bells and angels, submerging the Christmas tree in snow and tinsel, filling individual stockings with little titbits – not an easy feat in the immediate post-war period when the shops were still poorly stocked – and finally, on Christmas Eve, decorating all the breakfast trays so that when the great day finally dawned, it would be as much like home as possible for those confined to the ward.

Unfortunately, when we were all lined up ready to start our round of carol singing on Christmas Eve, our soloist was nowhere to be found. She was discovered at the eleventh hour, desperately trying to persuade an overenthusiastic young houseman to give her back her uniform! In order to calm down the Christmas fever which was creating havoc in the Children's Ward, tearing the nurses' patience to shreds as they perilously hung up swinging paper lanterns and attempted to disentangle miles of coloured streamers from the sticky hands of eager under-sixes, all convinced that they were helping, the young houseman had offered to bring his guitar and cool the general frenzy with some community singing. Just to make the place look even more like a three-ring circus, he'd borrowed Finch's cap, belt and apron. Of course the children were all delighted, but when it was time for her to join the choir which was already snaking round from the nurses' home in a crocodile, he'd rather fancied himself in his new attire and was loath to give it back.

By the time she'd finally persuaded him, over the protests of the children who all insisted that the additions vastly improved his appearance, he'd persuaded her that she needed a drink to moisten her vocal chords and, behind her back, poured out a glass of neat gin, betting her, with the full vocal support of the children, that she couldn't swig it down in one go. Finch had gulped down more than half before she realised what it was and when she at last staggered over to join the head of the crocodile, could hardly stand, let along walk.

Gert was beside herself, her eyes popping behind her steel-rimmed spectacles, her enormous feet raising dust on the hard concrete as she leapt angrily up and down, thundering out hellfire and brimstone on the unfortunate young houseman's head and when *in extremis* she paused for breath, threatening loudly to have him 'cashiered'.

We were all delighted at this unexpected touch of colour added to our evening and stifling our giggles, managed to prop Finch up between us with the result that the head of the procession was led by three nurses instead of two, one carrying a candle, one a music sheet and one bleary-eyed and hopelessly drunk in the middle, only kept on her feet by the firm pressure of her companions' shoulders: though we were all rather afraid that her breath might either put out the candle leaving us in the dark or, conversely, set the music on fire. A voice from the back was heard to whisper over-loudly as we frog-marched Finch to the door of the first ward that we didn't really NEED candles, her nose would light the way, to which remark Gert responded with more thunderous threats.

Mercifully, all this unexpected emotion didn't affect her singing of *A Virgin Most Pure* though her appearance did seem to be rather inappropriate. But the patients didn't seem to notice anything amiss, they were too busy crying their eyes out, though so much emotion was certainly not occasioned only by the purity of our voices. It was part of the general Christmas nostalgia which swept over them and a few elderly women propped up in bed completely reverted to childhood, Doris amongst them, sniffing through their tears and loudly proclaiming that we weren't nurses at all, we were angels!

In spite of everything we got through the so-called festive season with all the staff enthusiastically joining in the jollifications, and behaving completely out of context in a thoroughly unprofessional and unorthodox fashion. Our aloof RAS put on a tall chef's cap and carved the turkeys and the RAP helped him, wearing a garish paper hat and a frilly apron as he ran up and down the ward with heaped plates. The housemen got themselves into various music hall garments and everyone behaved like complete lunatics.

All the patients who'd been on strictly controlled diets for weeks ate enormous helpings of turkey and Christmas pudding, drank sherry as if it were going off the market, and consumed mince pies by the dozen, so that in the flat period between Christmas and New Year, we not only had the extra work of staggering up and down ladders removing decorations, which somehow wasn't half as much fun as putting them up, but the added burden of coping with all the gastric disturbances erupting in patients whose diets had, over the Yuletide truce, gone completely berserk. Though from what I heard, the damage in the men's ward was infinitely more devastating.

As none of the nurses was allowed a day off in the week running up to Christmas, there being so much to do, by the time January came round we were all beginning to feel slightly jaded and the blues were setting in.

Although, before I left London, Jane and I had promised to meet whenever we could on our days off, they had never so far coincided and I realised that since I arrived at the Annexe we hadn't managed to meet at all. We had kept in touch with the odd telephone call, trying to organise a get-together, but inevitably, the impossibility of meeting and our now different lifestyles had caused us to drift apart. But on New Year's Day the post brought me a lovely pale green silk scarf, obviously sent by her mother from South Africa, together with a little note.

Sitting on my bed I read her letter once again, remembering the talk we had had in her room not long before I left London, and my mind went to Father Hammond and the conversation I had had with him on the day Mrs. Forrest died. And suddenly I felt a flatness, a drabness, and I knew that it wasn't just the post-Christmas blues which were causing it.

The past few weeks had been hectically busy and I hadn't had time to think. Now, suddenly, it was all over and the New Year stretched pointlessly ahead. I looked out of the window at the expanse of no-man's land, the collection of huts, the bleak, bare, windswept winter landscape and suddenly my mood fell in line with my surroundings. I felt inside me the bleakness and emptiness which, in my frenzied activity of the past few weeks, I had tried to camouflage with work, to gloss over and to forget.

Glancing through Jane's letter again I saw that she was going in a party to a New Year's Eve ball in the large building opposite the hospital where the medical students were housed and I vaguely wondered whether, had I not been sent down to the Annexe, I might have seen the year end in a more exciting way.

I remembered the Regimental Ball I had attended just one year ago; it seemed like a lifetime away. And inevitably, my mind went to my brother Geoffrey.

"HE probably spent his New Year's Eve in a fox hole in the jungle," I muttered to myself as I got up from the bed and went to change my apron. "So what are YOU feeling so sorry for yourself about?"

But I was sorry for myself all the same.

When I went back to the ward Sister called me over to where she was fixing a drip for a patient who had suffered from an excess of Christmas fare.

"You're to go and help out next door in the Children's

Ward, nurse," she said, her deft hands firmly anchoring the bottle in place. "They are two nurses short."

I went back into the linenry and picked up my cloak and collection of cardigans. Crossing the short patch of grass which separated us from the ward next door, I wondered just how I was going to react to working with Morley-Watson. Even though my talk with Ogilvie had given me a glimpse as to why she was the way she was, she still rubbed me up the wrong way whenever we came in contact, and I mostly tried to avoid her. But when I walked in, she wasn't there and confusion seemed to be reigning.

"Sister's just been rushed off with an emergency appendix," a flustered blue-striper said as she dashed past me. "We were already one short and it's bedlam here at the moment."

Judging by the noise, it most certainly was: ALL the children appeared to be running obstacle races in their nighties.

Suddenly a wet sponge came flying through the air and hit me full in the face. It was followed by a slippery, soapy, naked little boy chasing after it yelling:

"Oh là là, comme ci comme ça, Nosey-Anne."

An angry and very excitable ward maid rushed after him shrieking:

"Dooglass, Dooglass, you nortee boy."

A split second later he whizzed past me again in the opposite direction still yelling "Oh là là," whereupon all the children who still happened to be in their cots leapt up and down joining in the chorus, until the poor blue-striper who'd been so suddenly left in charge rushed out of the bathroom and grabbed him.

"Come and give me a hand in here nurse," she called over her shoulder, "I've got three all soaped."

As I followed her a little blond boy with a snub nose standing up in his cot grabbed my arm.

"We've got a REAL lav'try at our 'ouse now," he said à propos of nothing, and added seriously, "wiv a chain."

"Have you?" I replied, intrigued. "What did you have before?"

"Dirty ol' bucket," he said matter-of-factly and letting go of my arm flopped back onto his bed tunelessly singing *Deep in the 'eart of Texas*.

I went into the bathroom, almost falling flat on my face as I slipped on a large piece of soap which had now been aimed at me.

"Little BEAST," Elliot hissed. "Here, grab a towel and cope with this one," and she hauled a protesting slippery body out of the bath. "He needs his toe-nails cutting, better have a look at his finger nails too while you're at it."

I sat down on a stool in the middle of a puddle, firmly anchoring the wriggling Douglas onto my lap. After I'd rubbed him dry I grabbed his hands and inspected them, but he quickly pushed them behind his back.

"Douglas," I said patiently, "I'm not going to hurt you: I just want to cut your finger nails."

He let out a terrible ear-splitting wail.

"Ow-ee-ow," he howled, his plump little body going through all kinds of terrible contortions in an effort to wriggle off my lap.

"You'll 'urt me," he wailed.

"Douglas, I promise you I won't."

He looked at me defiantly.

"You will."

"I've told you I won't."

He looked at me again, the wriggling slowing down.

"Swear God's honour?" he challenged.

"Oh, if you like."

"Go on, then, swear it," he insisted.

I solemnly swore.

"Now cross yer 'eart and swear to die if ya tell a lie."

I sighed exasperatedly and crossed my heart, whereupon he gingerly removed one hand, then immediately withdrew it again the minute I started to cut his nails.

"Douglas," I said, "you're going to get hurt."

"Told yer so," he said triumphantly, and promptly sat on both hands.

"Oh come on," I said, "don't be so silly, just let me try with one hand and you'll see."

The ordeal of one hand was almost too much but when I had finally managed the two, the thought of going through the whole performance again on his feet was just too much, and I gave up.

Once I had finally managed to squeeze him into his pyjamas he scampered off as Elliot handed me a plump little girl. She appeared to be quieter, and when I looked down at her I saw that she was a mongol.

I smiled at her, but she stared back blankly.

"What's your name dear?" I asked gently.

"Patsy," she lisped, and promptly stuck her tongue out at me.

Patsy didn't prove as docile as I'd at first imagined and refused point blank to put her head into her nightie in the orthodox way. She insisted on trying to force it through one of the sleeves. As we were struggling and I was slowly losing ground, Elliot shouted from the bathroom:

"Are you ready? Another one coming."

At that moment, all the lights fused.

"Oh NO," I heard Elliot groan, as pandemonium broke out once more in the ward. "Perhaps it won't be too long: we don't need to get out the candles, it's such a performance."

And she plonked another wet body on my lap, Patsy having won the tussle and escaped in the chaos. This time I had no idea which sex the horror was and by then didn't particularly care. I was soaked through and, as she left, Patsy had grabbed my cap and was now doubtless stamping it out of shape in some dark corner in retaliation.

The power cut didn't last too long and as the lights went up I saw that I had another little girl in my arms, but this time I didn't bother to ask her name, in case she too had some original way of expressing herself, perhaps even less pleasant than having a tongue stuck under one's nose.

With a quick grab and a rub I manoeuvred her into her nightie. I was getting adept at it now but did vaguely wonder why I had envied Jane being assigned to the Children's Ward whilst I had been sent to the comparative peace and order of Women's Medical.

Those thoughts were going through my mind when Douglas rushed back into the bathroom, without his pyjamas but wearing his socks, and fell headlong on the slippery surface. He let out another unearthly howl. As I put the unknown girl down on the floor, avoiding the puddles, and went to haul him up, the lights fused again.

I was beginning to understand the exasperation I had seen on Morley-Watson's face as she shovelled jelly down an unwilling toddler and wondered whether I hadn't perhaps misjudged her. Then it occurred to me that I hadn't seen her since I arrived and I wondered where she was.

Elliot came back into the bathroom; she obviously knew her way around in the pitch-black better than I did. I could barely make out the shapes in the gloom and what looked to me like small cupboards which jumped from place to place and hurled themselves across the ward, turned out to be 'sick' children.

"Better get the candles," she said desperately, "this could go on all night."

Blood-curdling moans and wails of "I'm a GHOOOOOOOOST", coming from Douglas, followed by piercing shrieks of terror from all over the ward, accompanied Elliot as she disappeared into the darkness, returning with a large box of candle ends and a pile of saucers. She was right, the cut lasted over an hour and when the combined glow of several candles finally lit up the ward it was to reveal most of the cots empty, though one of them contained no less than six bodies all fighting under the blankets and three others engaged in the same combat underneath.

Elliot produced two storm lanterns and we trooped around the ward grabbing wriggling, giggling pyjama-clad figures out of the most unlikely places and gradually restoring order. Patsy was captured as she made her bid for freedom, attempting to force the knob on the ward door, rather unsuccessfully as her head was still wedged firmly in the sleeve of her nightie where she had insisted on putting it. And a poor little soul, who had obviously just had a double mastoidectomy, was found shut in the toy cupboard, a wadge of bandages which should have covered her ears sitting drunkenly over one eye.

Just as we had got them all back into their respective cots and settled down for the night, light suddenly flooded the ward again and all the children promptly leapt up in bed and informed us of the fact.

The lights went up to reveal an absolute battlefield of teddies, rabbits, golliwogs and the rest. The children had obviously had a splendid time in the dark hurling their soft and not so soft toys at each other.

"Phew," said Elliot, as she blew out her storm lantern and started picking up the pieces, "this place looks like the city dump."

I laughed above the armful of stuffed animals I was carrying then tripped over a toy engine, sending it racing angrily across the floor until it crashed into a cupboard. They really had turned the ward into a disaster area.

"Hope that's the last power cut we have THIS evening," Elliot said. "ALWAYS happens when we're short-handed."

"Who else is missing besides Sister?" I enquired.

"Morley-Watson," she replied, adding curtly, "Douglas, SHUT UP," as he started again to conduct his chorus of "Oh là là, Nosey-Anne," imitating the rather highly-strung ward maid who hadn't stopped wailing "Oh là là" for the past hour.

"What IS this Nosey-Anne business?" I enquired as we stuffed all the discarded toys into the toy cupboard.

"Oh, it's Lucienne," Elliot replied exasperatedly, "our French ward maid. The children think she's called Nosey-Anne, or at least that's their version of her name, and they never stop teasing her. If ONLY she wouldn't rise to the bait all the time they'd stop it. DOUGLAS," she broke off, "I'M WARNING you!"

Douglas was still chanting, "Nosey-Anne, oh là là", but he finally understood that Elliot meant business and flopped back in his cot, pulling the bedclothes over his face.

"Little devil," she said smiling, "he's adorable really."

I smiled; then I remembered what she'd said about Morley-Watson.

"What's the matter with Morley-Watson?" I asked.

"Got a terrible rash, all over her body."

Elliot sighed.

"Just at the moment of course when we're run off our feet. She's been having injections for that chronic catarrh of hers and they've only just found out that she's allergic to them. You should see her, looks like a spotty boiled lobster."

"Poor old thing," I said.

Morley-Watson was hardly an oil painting, but if now she looked like a spotty boiled lobster...

"Is she going to be warded for long?" I enquired, wondering just how long I was going to be subjected to this Lilliputian torture.

"Oh, at least ten days," Elliot replied, "if not two weeks, then she might have to convalesce. Should say you're here for three weeks or more."

She broke off abruptly and pounced across the ward to where Douglas was busy sticking lumps of brightly coloured plasticine all over his counterpane.

"Douglas," she screamed, all restraint finally gone, "I'll MURDER you."

At that moment Miss Welly walked in.

Elliot stood frozen to the spot, and I slipped hurriedly into the bathroom so that she shouldn't see my nakedness. I still hadn't discovered what Patsy had done with my cap.

"I'm sorry Sister," Elliot said, her eyes following Miss Welly's as they swivelled disapprovingly round the ward, "I'm afraid we've had a power cut and the children got out of hand."

Miss Welly looked down her nose icily, implying that children under her control NEVER got out of hand. Her cold disapproving eyes looked like two poached eggs.

I noiselessly pulled the bathroom door to. Morgan-Davies was paddling around trying, not entirely successfully, to cope with the flood.

"Here," she hissed, throwing me a floor cloth, "grab that and set to. What on EARTH did the old bag have to come round NOW for?"

"Dunno," I said suppressing a giggle, hoping against

hope that she wouldn't decide to inspect the bathroom.

Morgan-Davies peeped through a crack in the door.

"Oh good," she said, "she's going over to Patsy's bed. She ADORES Patsy, goodness knows why. That'll sweeten her up a bit and perhaps she won't bother to poke her nose around and see what we're up to. By the way, where's your cap? You'll be for it if the old girl sees you."

"I know," I answered grimly. "Patsy!"

"Nuff said," she answered. "Patsy isn't as half-witted as she appears."

But fate was not on our side that evening. As Miss Welly approached Patsy's bed, her face broke into what, for her, passed for a smile. But it was obviously one of Patsy's bad days; she had been decidedly put out at finally being obliged to stick her head through the right hole in her nightie and now she was determined to have her revenge.

As Matron bent over her cot, Patsy turned deliberately on her face, stuck her bottom in the air and made a very rude noise.

Miss Welly straightened up at the same time as a hard lump of plasticine aimed from the direction of Douglas's bed shot through the air and hit her bang on the nose, sending her rimless glasses wobbling perilously.

Morgan-Davies quickly closed the bathroom door and we both stuffed our fists into our mouths, trying unsuccessfully to stifle the giggles which were bubbling up uncontrollably inside us. But at that moment Miss Welly obviously decided that she'd had enough of children and, with an icy glance at poor Elliot, stalked from the ward, her Zorro cape streaming out ceremoniously behind her.

"Oh là là," said Elliot, imitating Lucienne as she poked her head round the bathroom door, "thank heaven the Charge Nurse will be back in the morning, this playing Sister is proving too much for me. You two managed to cope with the great flood?"

"Just about," Morgan-Davies said, giving a final wring to her sodden floor cloth.

"Good," Elliot went on, throwing in an armful of baby clothes and hand-knitted woollies. "There's this lot to be washed and put to dry before the Night Ass. comes round."

Morgan-Davies and I bent down and sorted through the collection of small garments, then set to on the evening's hand washing.

"Kids," she said with a snort, as we hung up the last things on the line, "puts you off marriage for good, doesn't it, working here?"

I laughed and wiped my hands on the rough roller towel.

"I prefer it to the alternative," I said.

Morgan-Davies looked at me in surprise.

"What's that?" she asked.

"Ending up like Miss Welly."

We both laughed and then looked at each other and let out a sigh of relief; thanks to the combined antics of Douglas and Patsy we'd managed to avoid a confrontation with old Wellyboots.

Little did I realise as we tiptoed back into the now dimly lit ward and looked down unbelievingly on the angelic faces of the twenty sleeping children who had finally decided to call it a day, that the rocket I had just avoided would boomerang and that my next and final confrontation with Miss Welly would be a dramatic occasion when, even though I did not utter one word, the whole course of my life would take an abrupt about-turn and I would stagger from her presence stunned and bewildered to pick up the pieces of my life and begin yet once again.

CHAPTER SEVENTEEN

Unexpected Decisions

As I was having breakfast the next morning, Elliot came and sat down beside me. She seemed embarrassed.

"I say Baxter," she said after a few minutes silently ploughing through her powdered scrambled egg, "what day off are you supposed to be having this week?"

I looked up over the rim of my cup.

"Thursday," I answered. "Why?"

She bit her lip and looked around.

"I wonder if you'd mind awfully if I asked you to change?"

"Well, I had made arrangements," I began, but she broke in.

"It's just that with Sister AND Morley-Watson off sick life has become a bit complicated and I'm going to have to ask you to take Morley-Watson's day off otherwise I don't know HOW we're going to work out the rota."

I sighed.

"I'm awfully sorry," she went on apologetically, "but I can't ask Mathews."

"Why not?" I interrupted, "after all Mathews is part of the ward team, not me."

"Well, she asked for that particular day months ago: her mother's getting married."

"Her MOTHER?" I expostulated.

"Yes," Elliot continued, "her father was killed in the war and her mother is marrying again. She's an only child and naturally her mother wants her to be there."

I sighed deeply, feeling very sorry for myself.

"Oh well," I said, "I suppose I've got no choice."

"I'm really sorry," Elliot went on, "but the circumstances ARE rather unusual."

"Oh all right," I answered grudgingly. "When is Morley-

Watson's day off?"

"Tomorrow," she replied.

"TOMORROW?" I exclaimed.

She nodded.

"'Fraid so."

"Doesn't give me much time to make alternative arrangements, does it?" I burst out angrily.

"Look here Baxter," Elliot broke in exasperatedly. "This is an emergency. I've said I'm sorry and that's all there is to it. Now we'd better be getting on or we'll be late."

She got up from the table and flounced towards the door, and I suddenly felt ashamed of my pettiness: poor old Elliot was having more than her share of responsibility and it couldn't be easy. It's true I had vaguely made plans to go to the theatre in London, but nothing had been finalised and it could easily wait till next week.

Hastening my step I caught up with Elliot as she walked across the concrete towards the ward.

"Sorry," I said. "'Fraid breakfast is not my best time of day."

She looked round and grinned.

"Mine neither," she replied and we pushed open the door and walked together into the ward. The previous evening's chaos didn't seem to have improved.

Billie, the sweet-faced little boy who was so proud of his new lav'try, was standing up in his cot draped in his blue and white checked counterpane, a pillow perched precariously on his head.

"Hooray, here they come," Douglas yelled as we entered, and began furiously jumping up and down on his uncomplaining mattress.

"We're playing a new game," Billie announced, his china blue eyes shining. "We're playing Jesus."

I was a little taken aback, and didn't quite know what to reply. It seemed rather blasphemous.

"I'm Jesus," he ended shyly.

"And I'm the Angel Gabril," Patsy piped in.

"No you're not," Douglas roared angrily, jumping more vigorously than ever. "I'M the Angel Gabril, you're Mary."

"I don' wanna be Mary," Patsy wailed collapsing onto her bed, one sock on and one sock off. I WANNA BE AN ANGEL."

"Well you can't," Douglas yelled back, thereby putting paid to any further argument.

"You can be the Angel Gabril NEXT time Patsy," said the gentle Billie, his pillow wobbling dangerously as he turned in her direction. I vaguely wondered why he imagined the character of Jesus should wear such an extraordinary headpiece.

"No she can't," Douglas roared, the bouncing which had somewhat subsided taking off with even more fury.

"I can, I can," shrieked Patsy, almost hysterical by this time.

"Chair, hat, bath, porridge, head," shouted a plump little toddler sitting in the playpen showing off his vocabulary while busily engaged in pulling the buttons off his pyjamas. And he rolled over, helpless with laughter at his own wit. "Funneee, funneee, funneee," he chanted over and over again.

The noise was deafening and I couldn't for the time being see what he found so amusing.

The Night Ass. swept in from the bathroom and, grabbing him from the playpen, wedged him firmly under one arm before going over to where Patsy was now weeping loudly and wedging her under the other.

"Been one of those mornings," she said, casting her eyes upwards in a significant gesture. "Someone's been feeding them oats I think, they're all completely wild. Can you cope with the residue, they're SUPPOSED to be dressed, but most of them seem to have got undressed again."

She picked up Patsy's one remaining sock which she had just flung angrily onto the floor.

"As for this little madam..."

Elliot, Mathews and I started racing round attempting to put the wards to rights and calm the children down before the Charge Nurse, who we all desperately hoped would be refreshed and full of energy after her weekend off, should walk into the ward expecting to find it spick and span.

We only just made it.

* * * * * *

When I went off duty during the middle of the afternoon, I suddenly felt a bit flat. Not expecting to be free, I had geared myself up for a day off later on in the week, so this sudden, unexpected liberty had left me without plans.

Strolling rather aimlessly over to the nurses' home, I had hoped to find someone else who was also free and at a loose end, but as I went in it was strangely quiet. Even Sister was out, and only the gentle soporific hiss from the stove was there to keep me company.

It occurred to me as I undid my belt and took off my shoes that I might as well make use of my time by going for a walk to see what the surrounding countryside was like. The weather was still bitterly cold but at least it wasn't raining, so bundling myself up I hurried through the concrete jungle towards the gate and turned into the lane, without any very clear idea of where I wanted to go or what I intended to do when I got there.

As I tramped along everything was absolutely still. Nothing seemed to be moving or even awake; the whole earth was sleeping and only the click of my shoes against the uneven road broke the silence. It really was the wilderness, I reflected. In the distance I heard a car rattling towards me and, without looking round, automatically stepped into the hedgerow. But the car slowed down, finally stopping just in front of me, and Father Hammond's head appeared at the window.

"Can I give you a lift somewhere, nurse?" he asked.

I walked towards him.

"It's awfully kind of you," I replied, "but I wasn't really going anywhere. Just taking the air."

He smiled and turned the key back in the ignition, but then I suddenly changed my mind. It was true I wasn't going anywhere, but simply because there was nowhere to go: the only buses which passed the hospital were very infrequent and the last one had left at two o'clock, but if he was going into the town I could at least have a look round there and take the six-thirty bus back.

I put my hand on the window as he was about to wind it back up.

"If you're going into town, perhaps I could come with you," I asked.

"By all means," he said, getting out to open the passenger door for me.

"Where would you like to be dropped?" he enquired as we drove along the deserted road.

"It doesn't really matter," I answered, "wherever it's convenient to you. I've had my day off changed unexpectedly and so I have no plans. I thought I'd just explore the local attractions."

"I don't think that will take you very long," he smiled, and we drove on in silence for a while.

"What do you usually do on your day off?" he enquired pleasantly.

"Oh," I shrugged, "all sorts of things. Quite often I go up to London, but this time I think I'll just relax and read."

"Do you enjoy reading?"

"Very much," I answered. "The only trouble is the hospital library is rather thin and I think I've just about exhausted it... or all of it that interests me."

And we drove along in silence once again. I could just see the spire of the town church coming into view as we bowled down the hill when he spoke again.

"I've got quite a good library," he said. "If you'd like to browse through and see if there are any books that interest you, you'd be most welcome."

I looked at him warily, but he obviously understood what was going through my mind and laughed.

"I'm a pretty voracious reader myself," he said. "You needn't worry, they're not ALL theological tomes."

I laughed then, feeling rather embarrassed that he had so clearly read my thoughts.

"Well, if you REALLY mean it, I'd love to," I answered.

"I'm going home now," he went on. "Would you like to come with me?"

We had just passed the Catholic church and the small presbytery attached to it and I was surprised that he hadn't stopped.

"Isn't THAT where you live?" I enquired.

"Oh no," he laughed, "the priest lives there. I have a couple of rooms behind the High Street."

I was completely taken back.

"But aren't you the priest?"

"Not yet," he said, "I've got about seven or eight years to go. We're rarely given our own parishes before we're around forty. I'm still a curate."

"But we never see anyone but you in the hospital," I went on, intrigued.

"I'm responsible for the hospital," he replied, "and for the sanatorium down the road from you. Father McNee is not far from retiring age and he doesn't like to drive, so he deals with the things in and around the town."

"I see," I said, and we lapsed into silence again as he drove through the town and swerved into a quiet road running parallel to the High Street.

"Here we are," he said and he pushed open a door, standing aside to let me enter the small dark hall before he showed me into a cosy sitting-room cum study. There were bookshelves lining every available wall space and I could see what he had meant when he assured me that he did not only own heavy theological tomes.

"There now," he said poking the fire into a blaze, "make yourself comfortable, browse as much as you like."

Taking my coat, he pushed a large comfortable old armchair nearer the fire and switched on a reading lamp.

"Sit down and make yourself at home, I'm just going to see whether I've had any urgent calls since I've been out."

And he left me surrounded by this unbelievable wealth of literature.

I wandered round from shelf to shelf taking books down, leafing through them, putting them back, piling others up for a second perusal. I picked up one by a man called Graham Greene whom I'd vaguely heard of; the title intrigued me, it was called *The End of the Affair*. Little did I then realise how prophetic that title would prove to be! Sitting down by the fire I began to read, and so absorbed was I right from the start that I did not hear him come back into the room.

"Oh, so you're a Graham Greene fan too?"

I looked up startled.

"Not really," I smiled. "I've never read any of his before but I'd like to borrow this one if I may."

"Take several if you like. Here, if you want more of his I think I've got the whole collection; that's his latest by the way."

I watched as his long slim fingers ran along the shelves removing books.

"There," he said, plonking a pile down on the little table beside me. "That should keep you busy."

The clock on the mantlepiece struck five, and he looked up.

"Oh dear," he said apologetically, "how rude you must think me. I haven't even offered you a cup of tea and it's already five o'clock."

I half rose, embarrassed, feeling that I had perhaps outstayed my welcome, but he smiled.

"DO stay and have a cup of tea with me," he said, "if you're not in any hurry. I'm going to make one anyway, and nothing very dramatic has happened since I went out, so for the time being I'm free."

I sat back down in the chair and he plugged an electric kettle into the wall socket and disappeared, coming back a few minutes later with a tray bearing a lovely Georgian silver teapot and two delicate china cups.

I must have looked surprised as he poured the water into the teapot, because he smiled as he put it back down.

"This service belonged to my grandmother," he explained. "My mother gave it to me when she sold her home and went to live in the convent."

He sat back on his heels staring into the fire.

"I was awfully pleased to have it, it reminded me of my childhood: tea and crumpets by the fire with Mother after school," he ended with a laugh.

"Does your mother like living in a convent?" I enquired.

"Very much. My father died when I was eight and she found it very lonely once we had all left home: my brother is in the Navy, one of my sisters is married and living in Jersey and the other one is working in London. Mother felt that we none of us needed the home any more and it was really too big for her, so she decided to end her days with the nuns and be looked after for a change."

He paused.

"That's how I came to be the proud possessor of a silver tea service."

And he smiled as he handed me my cup

For a few minutes we sat one on either side of the fire in a contented silence, then suddenly I asked him the question I had been longing to ask ever since I got into the car.

"Have you any news of Mr. Forrest?"

Father Hammond put his cup and saucer down on the little table by his side and leaning back in the worn leather armchair, crossed his legs before he spoke.

"He's plunged himself into his work," he answered.

"And the little boy?"

"He's still with his grandmother."

I looked into the fire remembering the conversation we had had on that dark windy November night and how he'd said then that if ever I wanted to continue it... But the words refused to come.

"Is that a good thing?" I said at last.

He looked up.

"What? Jonathan being with his grandparents? Oh yes, I think so. There's always been a very good relationship between James and his in-laws and Audrey's younger sister is still living at home, so the child is in a family atmosphere, which is important, until James is able to come to terms with what has happened. He doesn't live far from them so he sees Jonathan quite often, though just how long he'll keep up that large house on his own remains to be seen."

"I wish I could understand," I suddenly burst out.

He looked across at me and said nothing.

"It all seems so UNFAIR," I said.

His blue eyes seemed to pierce right through me.

"Isn't that what you said to me on the night Audrey Forrest died?"

I was surprised that he remembered.

"Perhaps not in so many words," he went on, "but that was what you meant. You'd come up against one of life's greatest mysteries and you were looking for a cut-and-dried answer. I told you then that there wasn't one."

I nodded glumly, staring bleakly into the fire.

"God doesn't promise us a rose garden down here," he said slowly. "He says we will have tribulations but He promises to be with us. In the Bible it says more than three hundred times, 'Do not be afraid' and also 'I will be with you, I will never leave you or forsake you.' We don't know all the answers. We're not meant to. God doesn't hand us a map of our life, but He does promise that if we will trust Him and allow Him to take control He will guide us and give us His peace."

He paused and once again looked directly at me.

"That's all we can ask for here, and personally, it's all I need."

"What about Mr. Forrest?" I enquired grimly.

"When he finally capitulates and realises that it's all HE needs," he continued quietly, "then he will be able to remake his life and find peace: unless a man is sure who Jesus is, he doesn't have a foundation on which to build when the storm breaks and the pain is sharp. At the moment he's just going through the motions of living, running away from the truth."

He got up and refilled my cup.

"Do you remember Mrs. Lind?" he asked gently.

I nodded, afraid to ask for news.

"So you remember her attitude towards the sentence which had been passed on her?"

"Yes," I answered thoughtfully, "I could never understand it."

Then suddenly I felt I had to know what had happened.

"Do you have any news of her?" I enquired tentatively.

"No," he said thoughtfully, "but had she died I would

have heard. Once she left the hospital she was surrounded by her own church community. She's a member of a very warm loving free church in the next town and I know that the whole family were simply carried along by their prayers."

"Do you mean that perhaps…"

I couldn't finish the sentence, it seemed so preposterous; the doctors had been categoric, her prognosis was not much better than Mrs. Forrest's and she had refused radiation: she COULDN'T still be alive.

"That perhaps she might recover?" he finished the sentence for me. "Why not? Stranger things have happened. I don't think we should rule out the possibility of a miracle."

I put down my cup and leaned back in the chair, absolutely bewildered.

"But the doctors?" I began.

"Doctors are very wonderful people," he said quietly, "and I admire and respect them but… they are not GOD. And sometimes God has the last word."

All this was way above my head.

"You mean a MIRACLE could have happened to Mrs. Lind?" I gasped. "But I thought miracles were only things which happened in the Bible."

"That's what so many people think and that's probably why we see so few," he answered drily. "But Jesus did say, 'If you BELIEVE, you will do greater things than I'. Do you realise that? Greater miracles than He did, it's mind-boggling. 'In my name you will lay hands on the sick…'"

He paused and looked into the fire.

"I'm sure that the church community to which Mrs. Lind belongs HAVE laid hands on her," he said. "They believe in miracles, they take Jesus at His word. The trouble today is that most people think as you do, that what happened two thousand years ago in Galilee was a once-and-for-all happening, not an ongoing ministry. We forget that Jesus Christ is the same yesterday, today and for ever, the Bible tells us so: we forget that Jesus promised to leave His Holy Spirit with us when He ascended into heaven."

He leaned back in his chair, his fingertips pressed together under his chin.

"His Holy Spirit living in us," he went on dreamily, "praying for us, interceding for us, working through us. Oh, if only we could all stop being so hidebound, so Pharisaical, so bogged down by rules and doctrines and just accept Jesus at His word. If only we could be like little children, accepting that what their father says is the truth beyond any shadow of a doubt, we'd see some wonderful changes in our world."

I sat there stunned, unable to take in what I was hearing.

Suddenly the old clock in the hall struck six and I realised that the last bus back to the hospital would be leaving in less than half an hour.

I jumped to my feet.

"I must rush or I'll miss the bus back and then I really will be stranded."

I looked across at him as he unfolded himself from the depths of his armchair and I didn't want to leave; I wanted to stay, to hear more, to drink in all these wonderful truths, these promises from the Bible which had been read to me in church over and over again and which, until that moment, had meant nothing.

"Thank you SO much for the tea and," I bent and scooped the books up into my arms, "for all these books."

"I'll drive you to the bus stop," he said.

"Please don't," I answered. "It's just round the corner, I know the way and... I think I need the clear night air to get my thoughts straightened out: my head is reeling with all you've just told me."

He smiled and didn't insist.

"Let me at least get you a bag for the books."

As he showed me to the door he said quietly, "I know it can't always be fun to be incessantly surrounded by a crowd of people so do feel free to come and help yourself to my library, or just sit by the fire whenever you wish. You'll find the door open; just give it a push and make yourself at home. It doesn't matter if I'm not here."

I looked up at him gratefully.

"If you really mean it?"

"I do," he answered simply.

"Then thank you, I will."

And I ran quickly down the frosty road to jump onto the bus just as it was leaving, never dreaming that that one visit had set in motion a chain of events in my life over which I would no longer have any control.

CHAPTER EIGHTEEN

The Letter

The next morning as I lay luxuriating in bed, revelling in the fact that I didn't have to get up, that the whole day stretched lazily ahead with nothing that I absolutely had to do, my eyes wandered avidly to the pile of books which I had wasted no time in attacking the evening before. And I decided to indulge myself and spend the entire day reading.

The curtains divided and Ogilvie came in.

"Letter for you," she announced. "Looks interesting so I thought you'd like to have it."

And she handed me an aerogram postmarked Singapore.

"Thanks," I said as she hesitated in the doorway, obviously eaten up with curiosity.

"It's from my brother," I said, putting her out of her misery and, judging by the look on her face, also disappointing her. "He's in Kuala Lumpur with his regiment, but..."

I turned the envelope over in my hands.

"Looks as if he might be on leave in Singapore."

"Want some coffee?" Ogilvie asked. "I'm going to make some."

"Lovely," I replied as I took a hairclip and gently slit down the dotted lines of the flimsy envelope, eager to know Geoffrey's news. He was mostly up country in the jungle so his letters were few and far between and to receive one was a rare treat.

"You'll remember Peter Harrington," he wrote.

I didn't remember him but gathered he must have been either at school or at Sandhurst with Geoffrey.

"He's in hospital somewhere near you: got a bad attack of dysentery and they discovered he had TB, so he was shipped back. If you could go and visit him sometime I'm sure he'd appreciate it. His home's in Ireland so don't suppose he sees much of his people and it's bound to be pretty tedious stuck there. In for a long stint I suspect and will probably be invalided out afterwards so I don't imagine he's feeling too cheerful. The odd visit would cheer him up."

And he gave me the name of a military hospital situated about thirty miles away.

"Hmm," I said to myself as Ogilvie walked in with two cups of coffee and sat down on the bed, doubtless interested in the news that I had an eligible brother doing, as I had once thought, adventurous things, and eager to know more.

"What's the matter?" she asked.

"Oh nothing much," I replied, putting the letter on the bedside locker and sitting up. "Geoffrey wants me to visit a friend of his who's been invalided out by the look of things: he's a patient in a hospital in Midhurst. How he imagines I can get there, I don't know."

"You can borrow my bike if you like," Ogilvie grinned.

"Brilliant idea," I replied. "Thirty miles there and thirty miles back plus a sick visit in between. No thank you, I don't think I'm in that sort of physical shape."

"Oh, it's that far is it?"

"It's in Sussex," I said drily.

"Don't you know anyone with a car?" she enquired.

This was still the time of strict petrol rationing, and only people with priority cards could get any, so her question was not so odd as it might now seem.

"Not down here," I grimaced.

"There must be a local doctor, or a vicar," she went on thoughtfully, "or even an old lady who's allowed petrol to take her to the Mothers' Union or something who could give you a lift."

"Possibly," I replied, "but I don't happen to know them and anyway an old lady going to the Mothers' Union as you put it would hardly be issued petrol coupons to go to one thirty miles away."

"S'pose not," she sighed. "Oh well, just trying to be helpful. Here, pass me your cup, I've just got time to wash them up before going back to the grind."

"Oh leave them," I said. "I'll do it when I get up. By the way how's your chum Anthea?"

"Better I think. At least she no longer looks like a beacon light warning of a hole in the road: more like a corpse actually, they've smothered her in calamine lotion. Poor thing has a courtesy visit from Miss Welly twice a day."

Ogilvie giggled.

"Probably why she's still covered in spots," she ended, heaving herself off my bed and stretching. "If you're sure you don't mind washing these up, I'll dash. It's hectic on the ward at the moment; they haven't replaced you so we're running around like dogs with three legs. Pringle and I are having to do your work as well as our own."

"Well don't let them replace me," I remarked. "You don't know your luck being on a nice peaceful women's ward after chasing round after all those so-called sick children."

I threw my eyes heavenwards.

"I'd hate to meet them when they're healthy."

Ogilvie laughed as she walked through the curtain and I heard the swing door swish to as she hurried back to 'the grind' as she called it.

I lazily reached over for the book which I had almost finished the previous evening and started to read, but my mind kept going back to my brother's letter and that poor chap lying alone in hospital with no one around to visit him. But there didn't appear to be any solution. Cross-country travel was impossible, though as the crow flies it wasn't very far: it would mean going up to London and coming down again.

"Oh well," I said, settling back into my book, "it doesn't seem very hopeful for the moment, I'll drop him a line instead."

And with this thought, I dismissed the whole matter from my mind.

But the following week I did take up Ogilvie's offer and cycled down to the town to return the books.

As Father Hammond had promised, the house was unlocked. I walked in gingerly then knocked on the door of his study, but there was no reply. Opening it slightly, I peered in. The room was empty but the disordered papers on the desk, the slowly dying fire and the jumper hastily thrown over the back of a chair all indicated that he had left in a hurry.

I walked over and stood looking down at the fire, wondering whether I should stoke it or not. Picking up the shovel I scooped up some small coal and placed it gently on the dying embers, carefully raking and poking until it settled into a steady blaze. Then, placing the books I had brought back with me on his desk, I went over and began to search along the crowded shelves for replacements. I chose four and looked longingly at the fire, tempted to do as Father Hammond had said and 'make myself at home' in this cosy atmosphere, but decided against it. Slipping the books into my bag I was just going out of the room when the front door burst open and he came in.

"Hallo," he said warmly, "I wondered whose bicycle that was propped up against the railings. You ARE energetic."

He smiled and looked down at my bag.

"Come for a refill?"

"Yes," I answered diffidently, "I took you at your word. I do hope you don't mind."

"Not at all," he answered. "Do come back in."

"I was just leaving."

"Do you HAVE to?" he asked. "I had to rush out before breakfast to an old lady whose daughter thought she was dying."

I raised my eyebrows enquiringly.

"No," he laughed, "she wasn't. I arrived at the same time as the doctor and all she needed to bring her back to life was a couple of hot water bottles."

"I can't believe it," I gasped.

"It's true," he replied. "It's been a bitterly cold night, and at ninety her circulation isn't what it was so she'd got very cold, that's all. But her daughter panicked. Mercifully she called both the doctor and me, otherwise I'd probably have been completely taken in too."

He smiled.

"Funny," he said thoughtfully, "how we so often don't

think of the obvious. So, I'm ready for a cup of coffee. Will you join me?"

He opened his study door and ushered me back in but I hesitated, afraid that I might be imposing.

"You'll need something warm inside you if you're going to cycle back up that bleak hill in this wind," he said, and he once again plugged in the electric kettle.

I sat down by the fire and leaned back, revelling in the cosiness of the small shabby room, and relaxing before I had to brace myself for the journey back and the return to duty.

As I waited whilst he fetched coffee cups Ogilvie's words came into my mind. "Don't you know a doctor or a vicar or someone who might have unrationed petrol?" I suddenly realised that although *I* didn't exactly know anyone, Father Hammond seemed to know everyone and might well have one of his parishioners who had to go in that direction from time to time and would give me a lift. Peter would obviously be in the hospital for some months, so there was no urgency.

He handed me the coffee and once again sat down in the chair opposite, leaning back and crossing his long legs.

"I hope you're going to have a good lunch after missing your breakfast like that?" I said.

He laughed.

"Mrs. O'Connor wasn't exactly trained at the Savoy, but she does very well, especially when she can never be sure what time I'll be in for meals."

"Are you often called out at odd times?" I enquired.

"Not at odd times," his eyes twinkled. "Just at mealtimes. It must drive her mad, but she never says anything."

He reached for his cup.

"Did you enjoy Graham Greene?" he enquired.

"Very much," I replied.

"He's a convert to Catholicism," he went on.

"So I gathered." I said and added, "Do you have many converts?"

His eyes twinkled again over the rim of his cup.

"Do you mean me personally?"

I laughed.

"No, not really, though I suppose you do. But generally speaking."

"Generally speaking, I think we gain as many as we lose."

"But I thought you couldn't lose," I exclaimed in surprise. "Once a Catholic, always a Catholic."

His eyes stopped twinkling and he looked grave.

"No," he said slowly, putting down his cup, "it's not quite as simple as that."

I glanced at my watch and knew that I should be leaving, but the idea which had come to me earlier would not go away and I decided to take the plunge.

"I wonder whether you know anyone," I began hesitantly, "one of your parishioners perhaps, who has to go to Midhurst from time to time by car."

He glanced across at me enquiringly and I told him about Geoffrey's letter.

Father Hammond looked thoughtful.

"Midhurst," he said looking up at the ceiling, his fingertips pressed together. "No I don't think so."

"Oh, it doesn't matter," I cut in hurriedly, "it was only a thought. One of the nurses jokingly suggested I find a doctor or a vicar or an old lady who was allowed petrol to drive me, so just in case you knew any old ladies in that situation, I thought I'd ask you."

And I laughed, embarrassed and sorry I'd spoken.

"Thank you so much for the coffee," I said getting up, "and... thank you for the books. I've brought back those I borrowed last week and left them on your desk. I took you at your word and helped myself to four more."

And I held up the bag for his inspection: but his mind seemed to be elsewhere.

"Yes, yes, of course. DO help yourself any time," he said and walked with me to the door.

As he opened it he suddenly turned round and faced me.

"Nurse," he said slowly, "if you like I could drive you to Midhurst."

"Oh no," I mumbled, now terribly embarrassed, angry with myself for ever having broached the subject. "It's terribly kind of you to even think of it, but I wouldn't dream..."

"No," he cut in, "I mean it. We can go next week if you're free."

I hesitated, not knowing how to get out of this awkward situation and mentally cursing Ogilvie for ever having put the idea into my head.

"It would have to be on your day off," he went on thoughtfully, "otherwise we couldn't do it in the time."

He paused and smiled down at me.

"I usually try to take Wednesday off; it's a good day for both hospitals as they have afternoon visiting so I don't need to be there. Would Wednesday suit you?"

His suggestion had taken me aback and I didn't know what to say. It just happened that Wednesday was my day off the following week and how I wished that it wasn't. It would have been so easy to say that I was off on Friday or Tuesday or any other day and so put an end to the conversation.

"Wednesday IS my day off next week as it happens," I heard myself mumbling, "but I really can't..."

"Why not be simple?" he said quietly. "You want to visit this young man in hospital: I have petrol and I can take you."

"But you don't have petrol to go to Midhurst," I burst out.

"I can very well do one or two visits on the way," he said. "Don't worry, I wouldn't use the petrol I'm given in anything but an above-board way."

As he said this, I felt ashamed.

"I must go," I muttered, "I'm on duty at one."

"Shall I pick you up in the lane outside the hospital at about ten on Wednesday morning?" he enquired.

"But," I protested, "I don't think visiting will be allowed before two or three. Do we need to leave so early?"

"Only in order to put your conscience at rest," he smiled. "I'll make my visits on the way and get you there for visiting time."

I looked up at him and bit my lip.

Unsure what to say, with a hurried 'thank you' I fled,

quickly unhitching Ogilvie's bicycle from the railings and pedalling furiously down the road, wondering what on earth had possessed me to put the question to him, embarrassed, flustered and yet strangely thrilled.

At last, perhaps, I was going to have time to ask him all those questions which had been tumbling higgledy piggledy round and round in my mind like clothes in a spin-drier, finding no escape: those questions which I had begun to ask myself a year or two earlier, to which I was sure there was an answer. An answer which, something told me, this grave young priest had found and could pass on to me.

CHAPTER NINETEEN

Stephen

The following Wednesday morning dawned bright and clear. It had been a miserable weekend weatherwise; the bitter cold had receded, leaving in its wake a damp fog which seemed to pervade everything, turning our frilly caps grey and casting a gloom over us all. On the Tuesday it rained hard, but Wednesday morning was one of those rare, sparkling winter days when the sun rose and stayed high in the sky, sending a glitter onto the bare trees, a shimmer dancing in the air giving a glimpse of forthcoming summer. It was a day poised between winter and spring, which did not seem to fit into any category.

I sat up in bed and, seeing the sun streaming in through the curtains, soaking up the damp dark earth outside, I wanted to fling open my window and shout with joy: it was that sort of day, magical, fairylike, a miracle which no one would have believed could happen after the cold wet foggy ones which had preceded it: a day which could only be lived to the full, because it could not last.

When I walked through the hospital gates at ten sharp, the lane was deserted and I wondered what had happened. I had expected to see Father Hammond's old car waiting at the entrance but there was no sign of it and I felt an emptiness invade me as if the brilliant winter sunshine had suddenly been extinguished and Sunday's fog surrounded me in its place. Just as I was wondering what to do next, I saw a car glide slowly out of a siding further up the lane and stop just out of sight of the hospital entrance: the passenger door opened and I walked towards it, surprised at seeing nobody.

"Hope you didn't think I'd forgotten," Father Hammond said as I got in. "I didn't want to get too near the hospital or even be seen. I was afraid they might grab me."

He grinned and started up the engine.

"Can't be too cautious."

"Isn't it a glorious morning," he said as we bowled along, the sun streaming in through the front window. "The sort of day when it feels good to be alive."

I looked across at him curiously.

"Do you ever feel anything else?" I asked.

"You'd be surprised," he answered quietly.

And for a few minutes we drove in silence along the deserted lane.

"But I thought priests and nuns never felt low, never got depressed, that they had something which we ordinary mortals lack."

He turned to look at me.

"We're ordinary mortals just like everyone else," he said. "We're not vaccinated with some magic potion to stifle our emotions. We feel joy and pain in exactly the same way as anyone else does. It's rather like what I said to you when you regretted having become emotionally involved with Mrs. Forrest: if priests are incapable of becoming involved, of caring, of putting themselves in the shoes of someone who is suffering and suffering alongside them, then we've missed our vocation."

And we lapsed into silence once again as the car hummed between the bare hedgerows. But it was a comfortable silence until he suddenly cried out:

"Oh NO, what bad luck!"

I looked at him in surprise.

"Is something the matter?" I enquired.

He laughed shortly.

"Well, yes and no. Did you see that old lady walking two pug dogs?"

I shook my head.

"You can be sure that she'll have seen *you*," he answered. "She lives in the church."

I was even more puzzled, and he looked down at me and smiled.

"Well, not exactly as you'd think, she's a pillar of the

church; invaluable, really, she starches all the altar linen, does the flowers and polishes the brasses, but unfortunately she's an inveterate gossip."

I still didn't understand and he gave me a wry smile.

"It'll be all round the parish by this afternoon, no doubt beautifully embroidered, that I was seen driving through the town with a voluptuous blond!"

"But I'm NOT a blond," I broke in.

"That's just what I mean," he answered grimly. "Oh well..." and he swung the car round and in through an imposing pair of wrought-iron gates.

I had no idea where we were.

"First port of call," he announced and jumped out. "I won't be long. I promised you this would be a business trip and I'd make calls on the way, didn't I? There's the morning paper in the glove compartment if you want something to read."

And he disappeared inside a beautiful old house.

I sat there sunning myself, with no desire to read anything, just lazily enjoying the beauty all around me. The garden surrounding the house was magnificent. A wide stretch of lawn led down to a small lake with a weeping willow dipping gracefully into it and I wondered vaguely who he could be visiting in such an impressive property.

But the warm sun streaming in through the car window and the sense of peace all around was making me drowsy and I nodded off, only to be awakened by the sound of voices. Startled, not remembering for the moment where I was, I looked up to see Father Hammond standing in the imposing doorway talking to a nun.

He was holding a basket in his hand.

As he walked the few paces across the gravel and got into the car she waved. Winding down the window he put out an arm and waved back, then turned and drove off down the drive.

"There," he said, "first visit over."

"Visit?" I queried. "You were awfully quick."

He laughed.

"That's one of the advantages of a dog collar," he said.

"We can visit out of hours when the patients are not expecting us. One of my parishioners had a fourth daughter last night so I popped in not knowing whether to commiserate with her or to congratulate her."

"What DID you do?" I enquired.

"Nothing," he grinned, "she was asleep. That's why I was so quick."

"What a BEAUTIFUL old place," I breathed as we drove out through the open wrought-iron gates. "Who does it belong to?"

"I don't know who owned it originally," he answered, "but it's now a maternity home run by the nuns. I come here every morning to say mass for them and they often prepare me a picnic if I'm trying to get away somewhere quiet on my day off. So, this morning, I asked them if they'd make it for two."

He turned and grinned at me.

"All right with you? I know of an absolutely lovely spot, a real sun trap, just outside Midhurst where we should be sheltered from the least breath of wind."

"A picnic at this time of year?" I said incredulously.

He looked disappointed.

"Oh," I went on hurriedly, "I think it's a splendid idea, but it's not something I've ever done before in mid-winter."

"Well, let's see what happens," he replied. "If the weather breaks or you think it's too cold we can always find a pub somewhere; this area abounds in the quaintest ones."

I was completely bewildered by the turn events were taking and wondered if he were in the habit of having mid-winter picnics with nurses he met at the hospital: and then it occurred to me that perhaps he had offered to be my chauffeur in order to convert me. But in the months since I had met him he had answered my questions honestly and told me what he believed, but he had never tried to persuade me to go to church, never suggested that I attend the mass he said every Sunday morning in the little hospital chapel, never even guided me towards the religious or doctrinal books on his overcrowded shelves.

I looked up at him surreptitiously: his eyes were on the

road ahead, his hands steady on the steering wheel and he was humming a tune under his breath. All my preconceived ideas of a Catholic priest suddenly went out of the window.

Up till now he'd always called me nurse and I had called him Father, just as everyone else had done, but I noticed that today he'd avoided calling me anything at all. Today seemed to be set apart from any other day: we appeared to be on a completely different footing, in a different world in fact, and for a brief moment a thrill of happiness, which I had not felt for a very long time and once thought I would never feel again, surged through me, only to be just as suddenly blotted out, and I felt afraid.

He looked down at me and smiled and I had that uncanny feeling, which I had experienced in his study, that he could read my thoughts; but he didn't say anything and we drove along the narrow country lanes in a comfortable intimate silence.

"Does everybody call you Father?" I enquired at last.

"Yes," he smiled, "why do you ask?"

"No reason," I said and lapsed back into silence: but it was no longer a comfortable silence. It had suddenly become charged with electricity. At last he said quietly, "My name is Stephen."

I looked at him but his eyes were firmly fixed on the road ahead.

"Mine's Noreen," I answered.

There was a pause and then he replied softly, " I know."

I shook my head in bewilderment. How could he know? We had always had it drummed into us that we must be absolutely impersonal on the wards, only addressing each other as nurse or by our surnames in order to avoid any undue familiarity with the patients. I couldn't imagine how he could have found out; but suddenly it wasn't important.

Slowing down he drew the car off the road and bumped along into what, in summer, would have been a wooded glade: but the trees were stripped bare and yet it had a charm, a peace, and as we got out the air was soft and balmy, almost springlike.

Opening the boot he took out the nuns' picnic basket

and a couple of rugs.

"A bit risky to sit on the ground after yesterday's rain," he said. "It must still be damp, but there's a fallen log over there which looks pretty solid. I can spread one rug on it and the picnic on the other."

And he proceeded to unpack the basket.

The nuns had certainly gone to a great deal of trouble and, seeing the food spread out on the rug before us, I suddenly realised that I was very hungry.

Stephen was wrestling with a large thermos flask.

"Shall we wait for coffee," he enquired, "and have it afterwards, or would you like it with the sandwiches?"

"Let's have it with the sandwiches," I answered and I took two buff-coloured bakelite cups out of the basket and put them with the rest of the food on the rug before us.

As we sat on the log eating our lunch we didn't talk much; it was pleasant just to bask in the sun which came streaming through the bare branches dancing jerkily over the damp grass. I could hardly believe it was January and sat there revelling in this unexpected change of weather, this wonderful bonus right in the middle of what had been predicted as a very hard winter.

"Are we far from Midhurst?" I asked at last.

"Just on the outskirts," he replied. "Do you want to be moving on?"

He glanced down at his watch.

"It's ten to two."

"I'm afraid I don't know what time visiting is, but I imagine it will be sometime between two and four."

"Let's get going then," he said, getting up and beginning to pack the remnants of the picnic back into the basket.

"I can't believe our luck, can you?" he smiled.

"What, the weather?"

"Yes, when you think what it was like last week at this time."

I nodded.

"I just stayed home and read last Wednesday," he went on, "there didn't seem to be any point in doing anything else."

And slamming down the boot of the car, he opened the door for me to get in.

"Next stop the hospital," he announced and added with a laugh, "but we've got to find it first."

However, it wasn't difficult.

"How long do you think you'll be?" Stephen asked as he dropped me at the gate.

"I've no idea," I replied. "What are you going to do?"

"Oh, I've got one or two things to see to." He looked at his watch. "If I come back for you at about three thirty, will that be all right?"

"Splendid," I said, and waved as the car moved away.

CHAPTER TWENTY

Questions Unravelled

As soon as I saw Peter of course I remembered him, though I don't know which one of us was the more surprised. He wasn't as lonely as Geoffrey had imagined since he was in a military hospital where there were many others in the same plight, far from home and family. They seemed to have formed a little community, those who were up keeping company with those who were in bed.

When I was shown in to his room he was sitting propped against his pillows talking to an attractive young Army nursing Sister.

"WHAT a surprise," he cried. "However did you know I was in here?"

"Geoffrey wrote and told me."

And we picked up the threads where we had left off.

He was able to give me news of my brother and of the war in Malaya, the conditions in which they were fighting, and although I'm sure he spared me the gory details, what I heard didn't exactly reassure me as to my brother's health and safety.

"It's all a big lottery," he smiled, "and survival is very much a question of chance, just as it is in civilian life. I shouldn't worry if I were you."

I promised not to, though not entirely sure that I could keep my word.

"You might well be in here for a long time?" I ventured.

He smiled wryly.

"Looks like it," he replied. "Here or elsewhere, I've no idea – there's some question of my being moved."

"I'd like to come and see you again," I said as I got up to go, "so let me know if you're moved, won't you."

"Will do," he smiled and waved gaily as I left.

When I walked out of the hospital gate Stephen was waiting.

"Did they give you tea?" he enquired as he held the car door open for me.

"No," I smiled. "Did you expect them to?"

"Not really," he answered. "I've had a scout round and there's a place right at the end of the High Street which looks as if it does home-made cakes and scones. Like to try it?"

"I thought you were doing official visits when I was in the hospital?" I teased.

He grinned.

"I still had time to scout around," he laughed and jumped into the car.

We cruised through the town and pulled up in front of a small hotel. There was a bright fire burning in the cosy low-ceilinged lounge and we sat lazily in front of it, in a sleepy comfortable silence, while waiting for the promised cake and scones to appear.

When we left it was already dark. Stephen turned the car back in the direction of home but, just as the lights of the town came into view, he slowed down and looked at me.

"Do you HAVE to go back to the hospital?" he enquired.

"What do you mean?" I asked.

"Well, have you a particular reason; do you have anything special to do this evening?"

I hesitated, a feeling of immense happiness flooding through me only to be immediately followed by a hollow despair. But I ignored it.

"No, not really," I heard myself replying.

"Would you come out to dinner with me?"

I hesitated again.

"There's a very pleasant restaurant not far from here where I often go with my sister when she comes to visit," he went on. "I'd like to take you there if you'll come."

Once again that surge of happiness poured through me and I found myself saying, "Thank you, I *would* like to."

He pressed on the accelerator and drove round the town, avoiding the centre, until we were out on a straight stretch of road. And again I heard him singing that same snatch of tune.

The restaurant was indeed pleasant. As he gave the order and we sat opposite each other in the warm discreet atmosphere I looked across at him.

"All this has come out of Mrs. Forrest's death, hasn't it?"

He raised his eyebrows enquiringly.

"My asking you that evening she died about the problem of suffering."

He took a bread roll and began to crumble it thoughtfully between his fingers.

"We never did finish that conversation, did we?" he replied.

"No," I said. "I think you rather left it open for me to take it up when I felt inclined."

He nodded.

"Do you want to now?"

"I don't know," I replied hesitatingly, and then suddenly I found myself telling him about Jane, our conversation that September evening, talking about my life in a way I had never done before with anyone. All the pain and bewilderment, the unanswered questions, came tumbling out while he sat there gravely listening to me.

Suddenly I looked up at him and I couldn't believe what had happened, couldn't believe that I had so bared my soul, brought all my feelings out into the open: but he didn't return my gaze.

"You cannot erase the past," he said quietly. "You can only heal the wound which is left behind."

He took the pristine linen table napkin and spread it thoughtfully on his lap as the waiter placed the dishes on the table.

"But HOW?" I cried.

"By forgiving," he replied, picking up a spoon and serving me. "Only forgiveness can move us away from the moment of terrible pain. The worse you have been hurt, the harder it is: minor cuts and bruises are easy to forgive, but when you've been torn apart inside it's harder and takes longer."

Stephen looked up at me.

"The only alternative is revenge," he said, "a never-ending escalation of hate and malice which merely freezes us, locks us into a cruel moment of our past. Forgiveness moves us away from that moment of pain, unshackles us from that endless chain reaction and allows us to start afresh."

He smiled kindly at me across the lamplit table.

"But when we forgive," he went on, "we are able to create a new beginning out of past pain, though it's almost impossible to do it alone. Our natural instinct is to lunge out and hurt back."

There they were again, those words which Jane had pronounced on that September evening. She had talked about forgiveness bringing healing.

"Forgiving is only for people who can accept the fact of unfair pain," he said gently, "as Jesus did: and we need His help if we are going to do it unconditionally, if we are going to be able to do it at all."

He laid down his knife and fork and looked away beyond me, beyond the heavy curtains drawn against the dark winter's night.

"And yet," he said, and his voice as well as his thoughts seemed to be far away, "if from the height of that tree where they nailed Him, even though He was innocent – if as He hung there bruised and bleeding Jesus could not only forgive those who had crucified Him, but ask His Father in Heaven to forgive them also, how can WE ever refuse to forgive another human being?"

He leaned back in his chair, his gaze still on some distant horizon, as the waiter arrived at our table holding a flaming copper frying pan.

"Jesus told us to be kind and compassionate to one another, forgiving each other just as He in God forgave us," he murmured.

He smiled very sweetly across at me and his whole face seemed to be luminous, radiant, shining with an inner peace and joy which I had never seen on anyone's face before.

"Knowing this, knowing what Jesus has done for us," he ended, "can we refuse?"

There were other diners in the room and their muted conversation rose and fell around us but at that moment it was as if we were alone; everyone else had been blotted out and the silence between us was electric.

"But Jesus was GOD," I cried.

He shook his head.

"That's where you're wrong," he said slowly. "He was wholly man and wholly God: but at the end, during those last three hours, as He hung on that cross in terrible agony, cut off from His Father, He was ONLY man: otherwise He couldn't have borne the sins of the world on His shoulders and opened the gates of Heaven to us all."

He paused and once again that tell-tale muscle moved in his cheek.

"He suffered and He died just like the criminals hanging on either side of Him," he went on softly, almost inaudibly, idly crumbling his roll again. "And when we forgive the hurt we never deserved, we walk in step with Jesus."

Stephen smiled across at me.

"Forgiving is love's toughest work, because it seems so unnatural."

But I pushed aside my plate, refusing to meet his gaze, and looked fixedly down at the table, idly describing a pattern on the cloth with my finger nail.

"Have you told James Forrest that?" I asked tightly. "Have you persuaded HIM to forgive God for taking his wife away and leaving his little son motherless?"

He paused and took a deep breath.

"I think it's only when we begin to understand God's purpose for death that we understand the real purpose of life," he replied thoughtfully. "We ALL love life, we cherish it and we do everything we can to preserve it because our lives and the lives of those we love are precious and important to us. But these short, mortal, perishable human lives we prize so dearly are not the final form, not the highest form of life at all. At best they only begin to suggest what wonderful plans God has in mind for us in the future."

He looked up and his slate-blue eyes pierced right through me.

"Death is real. You and I know that only too well. But sometimes people are totally unprepared to cope with it. It's as if all their lives they are pretending to be immortal."

He paused as the waiter hovered over us, pouring coffee from a tall silver pot.

"But this life isn't all there is," he finally went on when the waiter glided silently away across the thick carpeted floor.

Stephen reached into his pocket and bringing out a small, worn leather-bound book, began to read from John's Gospel.

"'Whoever hears my word and believes him who sent me has eternal life and will not be condemned: he has crossed over from death to life.'"

I kept my eyes glued to the white starched tablecloth.

"There is another life," he said softly, closing the book and putting it back in his pocket, "a hereafter, a heaven for those who have accepted Jesus and received the forgiveness He paid such a terrible price to give us. If there isn't, then His sacrifice was in vain and the injustice and suffering we see all around us is for nothing."

He looked across at me and smiled.

"Jesus said while He was here on earth, 'No eye has seen nor mind conceived the joys he has in store for those who love him'."

And he passed his hand absently through his thick dark hair, that muscle once again working in his cheek.

"I don't think those joys are reserved entirely for our eternal life," he said slowly. "I think He wants us to have a glimpse of heaven while we're still on this earth."

"He wants us to live this life to the full but to hold on to it lightly, knowing that the space of time we spend on earth is infinitesimal. We're here today and gone tomorrow, finite beings strangled by time. But when we get to heaven, we shall see the pattern as a whole, not just piecemeal, and realise that sometimes death is a healing, not the tragedy it appears to be down here. This life is only the ante-chamber and yet most of us behave as if it's all there is."

My head was in a whirl, but the mounting tension inside me was defused by a sudden loud whinny, followed by an angry snort, coming from the middle-aged woman at the next table.

I glanced curiously across at her.

Her face, which resembled an enraged beetroot, was working like milk just coming up to the boil. It almost exactly matched the maroon shot silk, obviously pre-war, dinner gown into which her ample form, now flowing over the sides of her chair, had been squeezed. I remember thinking that she looked like a raspberry blancmange.

As my eyes met hers she stopped picking imaginary bones out of her trout and, nodding her corrugated waves indignantly, went rabbiting on to her companion, a retired military type with a bristling moustache and a bald pate across which feathery strands of ginger hair had been carefully smoothed. It looked exactly like a hard boiled egg decorated with anchovies.

I turned my eyes back to Stephen.

He didn't appear to be aware of the whinnies and snorts which were still being furiously exchanged at the neighbouring table. I wondered if, one day, his abundant dark locks would be stretched in anaemic strands across a shiny bald patch, and the thought sent a shiver down my spine.

His eyes met mine and he smiled.

"God has made us in His image," he said, leaning across the table towards me.

I glanced at our neighbours and had my doubts.

"Each one of us is His own special creation," he went on, "unique and precious in His sight. He wants us to live with Him for ever in eternity and taste those joys Jesus told us about."

He looked across at me earnestly.

"Don't you want to share those joys?" he asked.

His words set my mind whirling once again, the momentary diversion obliterated. He had probed deep into my heart, bared my thoughts, revealed my pain and now he was offering me heaven on a plate, or so it seemed. Suddenly I was angry. It all seemed too trite.

"Are you trying to convert me?" I asked drily.

Stephen looked at me for a long time.

"I can't convert anyone," he said softly at last. "Only the Holy Spirit working in a person's heart can do that."

"But I thought ALL Catholics wanted to convert us infidels," I said ironically, ignoring his remark on the Holy Spirit which had rather embarrassed me.

"What a lot of misunderstandings there are in the world," he said, shaking his head sadly, "especially in the Christian world. Everything becomes distorted."

He wiped his mouth with his napkin and laughed shortly.

"Like my parishioner with the pugs."

For a moment we sat in silence, then he leaned across the table and smiled.

"I don't necessarily want to bring you around to my way of thinking," he said softly.

He paused and reached for my hand. "I just want you to meet Jesus."

"But what about suffering?" I said tightly.

"Suffering is a part of life," he replied gently, releasing my hand.

I opened my mouth to protest but he cut in on me.

"We only see through the window of other people's lives, not what really goes on inside. Suffering comes sooner or later to us all; but it's not *God's* way for us, he doesn't make us suffer. Very often we bring it on ourselves."

That defensive anger which had churned inside me earlier on and which his gentleness had quietly defused, suddenly foamed to the surface and boiled over. His words had cut me to the quick and I tightened my lips into a hard straight line. How DARE he pontificate to me? How DARE he suggest that pain was self-inflicted? Jane hadn't brought her suffering upon herself and neither had I. It was the war.

Still smouldering inside I refused to meet his gaze and turned towards our neighbours. They had stopped snorting at each other and were now heaving themselves out of their chairs, grunting heavily. As Colonel Blimp marched between the tables, like a battleship forging a passage so that the convoy could get through, I half expected him to hand out leaflets protesting against the outrageous state of affairs in the Punjab or the appalling sewage system in Wapping or Chipping Sodbury. His companion waddled behind him looking, now that she was upright, more like a tottering raspberry jelly than a wobbly blancmange.

As the door closed behind her ample form I felt Stephen's eyes upon me. He leant forward and gently touched my hand, again willing me to meet his gaze.

"All suffering is from the devil," he said.

His stark words belied his gentle touch and startled me back to reality. I still hadn't been able to swallow the idea that the devil, who'd been depicted in my Sunday School books as a funny little man in a red track suit with forked tail and horns, might be real after all. To me he was still a mythical figure conjured up in the minds of grown-ups to jerk hyperactive children into obedience. And yet here was this priest talking about him as if he actually existed!

I kept my eyes fixed on the white tablecloth.

"But Jesus came to relieve us of this terrible burden of pain and suffering," he went on gently. "He wants us to hand over our load to Him, to let Him guide our lives into the path which He chose for us before the beginning of time. Did you know that God planned your life so long ago?"

Stephen paused and looked directly at me, pushing aside his coffee cup.

"That's how much He loves you. And all He asks in return is that you should open your heart and let Him come in, heal your wounds and be your Saviour."

He put his elbows on the table and cupped his chin in his hands.

"It's not much to ask, is it?"

But I didn't reply.

I knew that that was what I really wanted, someone supreme to come into my life, clear up the mess and make me whole: but I was afraid, at that moment, of what it might cost me.

As I had done before when face to face with a decision which I knew could change my whole way of life, I evaded the issue and looked at my watch.

"It's getting late," I ventured.

He smiled and signalled to the waiter for the bill.

"And Home Sister will be rampaging all over the hospital looking for you behind every dustbin," he teased.

I shook my head unbelievingly. He seemed to know more about us than we did ourselves.

As we left the restaurant and got back into the car for the short drive to the hospital I suddenly didn't want the day to end: I wanted to go on in this atmosphere of warmth and peace and security which I felt all around me at that moment. I didn't want to go back to the ward, to the children, their noise and mess; I just wanted to drive on and on and never stop.

Stephen was again humming in the seat beside me and I recognised the tune from a record by Jean Sablon which Jacques had brought back for me after one of his trips to France. It was *J'attendrai*, a song which had been sung in the streets of Paris as the Germans marched in to the city in June 1940, and without realising what I was doing I began to sing the refrain.

He looked down at me and smiled and I suddenly felt embarrassed.

As we drew into the lane leading to the hospital I asked, "Do you usually invite your parishioners out on your day off?"

"You're not my parishioner," he replied, without taking his eyes off the road.

"Well, the nurses at the hospitals you visit, then."

"No," he said quietly, "I've never done it before."

He drew up just before we reached the hospital gate.

"But," he said hesitantly, "if I may, I'd like to do it again. This has been a very special day."

I turned and looked up at him, not knowing what to reply.

He opened the door of the car and came round to my side.

"Did I get you back in time?" he teased.

"Just," I laughed as I stepped out, then I hesitated, feeling awkward. "I really don't know what to say."

"Then don't say anything," he answered. "Except that you forgive me for preaching at you."

I looked at him standing above me in the moonlight. For a brief moment our eyes met, then I tore mine away.

"Thank you," I whispered hoarsely. I ran swiftly towards the hospital gate and pulled the bell, conscious of him still standing there looking after me.

As the porter shuffled out to open the door I saw another figure beside him under the light.

It was Miss Welly.

She glanced at me coldly, then looked pointedly down the lane to where Stephen was just starting up his car.

"Good night nurse," she said frostily and turning abruptly walked away, her grey cape floating out behind her among the silent huts like an indignant ghost.

CHAPTER TWENTY ONE

A Moment of Eternity

As I walked into the ward the next morning I was hailed by Douglas. He was riding the decrepit old rocking horse which was such a favourite with the children, rocking vigorously backwards and forwards, his arms round Patsy, who was sitting in front of him triumphantly manhandling the reins. I was surprised to see them together as they usually fought furiously over everything but occasionally, both being six and the oldest in the ward, they joined forces and called a truce: and this morning was obviously one of those days.

"Looka' us nurse," he yelled, and he bent his head forward and rocked even more hair-raisingly, provoking delighted screams of terror from Patsy, who seemed to be under serious threat of being catapulted straight over the old nag's head and into the fire.

"We're ridin' together," he gasped.

More energetic rocking and panting.

"REAL genl'men take lidies for a ride, don't they nurse?"

I smiled, thinking 'Out of the mouths of babes and sucklings', but just then a flustered night nurse poked her head round the bathroom door.

"Can you go and feed Marlene?" she called.

Marlene was a three-month-old baby who had been admitted suffering from malnutrition a few days earlier.

Going into the side ward where Marlene had been isolated away from the other children's racket and dangerous shows of attention – Patsy had been caught trying to climb into the cot to show her a picture of a donkey – I picked her up, and sitting on a low chair by the window started to feed her.

But it wasn't easy. She was listless and slow and it was

some time before I could even persuade her to take the teat in her mouth, but she finally settled down and I sat with her cradled in my arms, listening to the soothing sucking sounds in direct contrast to the noise coming from the main ward where everyone was racing round trying to get the place shipshape before the Charge Nurse arrived. Hearing the general hullabaloo I gathered that the children, refreshed after their night's sleep, were being their usual obstreperous selves.

My eyes wandered to the window and I found myself looking into the ward of which I had so recently been a part. As I did so, a tall figure in clerical black walked through the small door and into Sister's room. Seeing him my heart missed a beat and then began to thud wildly. When I realised that my pulse rate had risen dramatically and my heart was fluttering about somewhere in my throat, I felt suddenly angry with myself.

"This is RIDICULOUS," I muttered, putting the bottle down on the floor and deliberately turning my back to the window as I put Marlene over my shoulder to wind her.

Elliot's head came round the door.

"Finished?" she enquired.

I nodded, not daring to speak: the pounding in my chest was refusing to subside and seemed to be suffocating me.

"Oh good," she said, "it's all a bit hectic this morning and Billie doesn't seem well at all. Can you come and give me a hand?"

"I'll just change her," I mumbled, turning away, "and I'll be right with you."

Elliot looked at me curiously but made no comment and went back into the ward.

As I laid the baby back in her cot I couldn't help stealing another glance at the window of Sister's room opposite. Stephen was standing with his back to me and I gathered that the mass was already in progress but the half net curtains prevented me from seeing any further.

The Night Ass. was standing by Billie's bed, her hand on his pulse as I walked back into the ward. He lay there limply, flushed and feverish, not at all his usual bright cheerful self.

She beckoned me over.

"Come and sit with him," she whispered, "he's fretful."

I sat down beside his bed and a small hand crept out from beneath the sheet and took hold of mine. His large blue eyes were over bright and as I bent to look at him more closely he let go of my hand and his arm crept up, imprisoning my neck in the crook of his arm.

"Stay with me nurse," he whimpered, and closed his eyes.

I looked round for the Night Ass., knowing the hundred and one things there must be still to do, but she nodded briefly for me to stay where I was. Billie must have felt my anxiety because his grip on my neck tightened, almost forcing my head down onto the pillow beside his. So I stayed and he seemed content.

After a few minutes, as the hubbub in the ward was gradually dying down and order was somehow coming out of the chaos, I felt his grip weaken and saw that he had fallen asleep. Gingerly releasing my neck I laid his arm beneath the sheet and gently stroked his damp yellow curls. He looked so angelic lying there helpless that it brought a lump to my throat as I tiptoed away.

"What is it?" I asked the Night Ass. when we gathered to report, jerking my head in Billie's direction.

"Another attack of nephritis," she said.

She sighed.

"Unfortunately with him it's chronic."

Billie slept most of the morning and most of the afternoon, but when I went back on duty the next day he was sitting up in his cot totally engrossed with two pieces of plasticine.

He looked up as I came in, his blue eyes now clear and sparkling.

"Look what I'm making for you nurse," he called out, jumping up and bouncing to the end of his cot. "A dinysore!'

And he waved the completely unrecognisable object at me.

I smiled down at him and ruffled his curls as I admired his handiwork, marvelling at the resistance of children.

They either seemed to be bouncing with health or at death's door; there never appeared to be any in between. And then words from my childhood, more passages from the Bible which I had been obliged to learn by heart, surfaced from my subconscious.

'Unless we become as little children, we shall not see the Kingdom of Heaven.'

I hadn't understood them at the time, but now I saw what they meant. Unless we have the absolute transparency, the simple unquestioning faith of little children, we cannot UNDERSTAND the things of God. And the thought came to me that perhaps healing was all tied up with simple trust. If we trusted this all-powerful God as simply as a child trusts – as Billie had trusted me when he asked me to stay with him yesterday morning, falling peacefully asleep once he knew that I was there holding him tight – perhaps the miracles Stephen had seemed to think were possible might happen. And I wondered if that was the kind of faith which Mrs. Lind and her family had, and whether that faith would be rewarded.

But at that moment little David popped his head over the top of a screen, looking rather like Mr. Chad, with his button nose resting on the rim, and said, "I lookin at you," and I realised that everyone was rushing around and I was standing daydreaming.

"Billie's not allowed up today," the Night Ass. said. "Can you wash him and get him ready for breakfast?"

I turned to where Billie had flopped back in his cot and was now intently gazing at the pictures in Douglas's Beano comic, smiling to myself as I went to the bathroom to collect all the paraphernalia needed to wash and change a four-year-old without actually getting him out of bed.

Later that evening, going round the ward and seeing children all sitting up in their cots, pink and angelic as they waited for their milk and biscuits before settling down for the night, I felt a sense of satisfaction and happiness pour through me and wondered why I had ever thought it would be easier to be on an adult ward.

The small square room with cots arranged around it in a

circle was very cosy compared to the long wards I had been used to with beds neatly arranged along either side. And after everything had been tidied for the night, the children finally settled, last cuddles given and favourite teddies and bunnies propped up in bed beside them, the light shaded and only the soft hiss from the stove to break the silence, there was a sense of peace and purpose as we crept around peeping into cots where children were sleeping soundly, exhausted with the tremendous effort of just being a child and the enormous 'duties' it entailed. Sometimes there was a hoarse whisper for a drink, which inevitably set up requests all round, but usually the day wound down peacefully and I realised that I was going off duty with a spring in my step, happy at the thought of returning to the ward again the next morning.

I didn't bump into Stephen around the hospital all that week and something held me back from going to exchange my books at his house: but on the following Thursday afternoon as I was coming off duty, he caught up with me before I crossed over to the nurses' home.

"Hallo," he said brightly. "Are you going on or off duty?"

"Off," I laughed, "just for the afternoon."

"Would you like to go for a walk on the downs?" he ventured. "It's a nice blustery day, blow the carbolic away."

I hesitated.

"I'll meet you in the lane in about twenty minutes," he said. "Is that time enough for you to change?"

I nodded. It WAS a lovely blustery day, not a bit like that sparkling one we had had almost two weeks before, but seasonal weather, grey and cloudy with a mild west wind. I hadn't any plans and a walk would do me good, I argued, trying to reason with myself.

As I stepped out into the lane his car slid up beside me; the door opened and without a word we drove off, bypassing the town and making for a lovely stretch of windswept downs.

"Isn't it gorgeous?" he said, breathing in deeply as we got out of the car.

I smiled and he tugged at his dog collar, then diving into

the back of the car he tossed it on to the seat, tying a scarf round his neck in its place.

"What ARE you doing?" I asked, intrigued.

He grinned.

"Avoiding the gaze of lady parishioners with two pug dogs," he said.

I didn't reply.

"Why don't you just wear civvies?" I enquired as we set off across the soft springy turf.

"I think my generation will finally get round to it," he answered, "but so far the old diehards don't approve."

He sighed.

"Officially, we're not allowed to."

"Whyever not?" I asked, puzzled.

"I don't know," he shrugged. "Just another man-made rule."

I looked up at him questioningly. The wind was lifting his hair, blowing it across his face, making him look almost boyish. All the strain and tiredness which I had so often seen etched on his lean features seemed to have suddenly disappeared.

He turned and smiled down at me then, softly humming that same old tune under his breath, he reached for my hand and taking it in his firm grasp swung it gently backwards and forwards between us as we walked together across the Downs.

Suddenly a dreadful fear seized me and I wanted to run away. The touch of his fingers had sent shock waves of electricity pulsating through me, yet his strong hand was warm and comforting and I didn't want him to let go: but I knew that I was approaching deep waters, waters which could completely overwhelm me and, once again, I was afraid.

"There's a tiny little café on the other side of this hump," he said at last, "where we could have hot scones and tea."

I hesitated and immediately felt his grip tighten.

"I have to be back on duty at five thirty."

"It's only half past three," he pleaded. "I promise I'll get you back in time."

So I surrendered.

"How do you know of all these places?" I enquired, as we sat in the cottage front room with a log fire burning brightly in the corner.

"Oh," he said, "I do a lot of walking. Need to get away from the parish at times otherwise it all gets on top of one."

He bent forward and buttered a scone.

"Occasionally," he went on, "I set out to do some visiting and I just can't face it so I drive onto the downs and walk for miles instead. Then I get back in the car and I'm able to go on. I suppose that's how I discover all these out of the way places tucked in the oddest nooks and crannies."

I looked across at him as I put down my cup.

"Is being a priest so difficult then?"

He ran his hand thoughtfully through his hair in a gesture I had come to recognise.

"Not being a priest, no. But sometimes trying to conjugate doctrine with my interpretation of what Jesus wanted us to do is not always obvious."

He sighed.

"Perhaps it will be easier when I get my own parish and can run things my way."

"Don't you get on with Father McNee?"

"Oh yes," he said, "that's not the problem. But he's nearly seventy and I'm not quite thirty-three: there's a whole world of difference in our understanding of things. He's pre-war, I'm post-war. He belongs to the old school, I suppose I'm one of the rebel brigade who wants to make changes."

He looked into the fire.

"It's not always easy for either of us."

As we returned to the car and set off on the drive back to the hospital we both seemed to be preoccupied with our own thoughts, but just before we slowed into the lane leading to the collection of huts I turned to him.

"If I want to have your faith," I asked, "do I have to become a Catholic?"

He took a deep breath and kept his eyes fixed on the road ahead.

"No," he said quietly, "Jesus didn't put labels on us, man did that. All you have to do is believe in Him, ask Him to come into your heart and be your Saviour."

He smiled gently down at me.

"God doesn't live in churches built by human hands," he ended.

As we drew up a few yards from the hospital entrance he turned to look at me, his slate-blue eyes shining, almost luminous.

"Christ in us, the hope of glory," he murmured. "It's almost more than the human mind can take in, isn't it? Jesus living in US, not in lumps of bricks and mortar."

He paused and when he went on his voice was hardly above a whisper.

"And when it happens we have the certainty of a life one day with Him in heaven, because the Bible promises us that whoever believes in God's Son HAS eternal life."

For what seemed like an eternity neither of us spoke nor made any attempt to move: there was an utter silence and stillness in the car and a peace which I had never known seemed to flow around me.

"I want to," I whispered in the end. "I want to have this assurance that you have, I want to have faith."

I paused, holding my breath, afraid to break that wonderful sense of something quite indefinable which seemed to be surrounding us like an aureole.

"I want to know your Jesus," I ended brokenly.

He looked down at me and for a moment said nothing, but I saw that tell-tale muscle working in his cheek and I knew that, for him, this moment was as charged with emotion as it was for me.

It was as if we were locked together in a universe apart, an unforgettable moment in time, poised on the edge of a precipice which could either catapult us into something which was beyond my wildest dreams, beyond anything my finite mind could understand, or merely leave us precariously hanging there in a kind of no-man's land with that feeling of unreality one experiences in a plane just before it lands: the breathless expectation, one minute flying through space suspended between heaven and earth, the next jerking back to reality as the wheels touch ground and the plane bumps across the tarmac.

Suddenly a great wave of emotion welled up from the very depths of my being and I began to cry, softly, uncontrollably. As I brushed my hand across my eyes he gently removed it and, still holding it in his, took his handkerchief and began wiping away the tears which were now streaming down my cheeks. And as he did so our eyes met.

I knew that I ought to leave, but I was unable to: his eyes held mine and all sense of time or reality seemed to recede. A feeling of overwhelming joy flowed imperceptibly around us, like a soft, gentle mist wrapping us together in the folds of its cloak, and cutting us off from the world outside.

But gradually I became aware that we were no longer alone; there was another presence looming menacingly out of the mist, and the aura, the unbelievable sense of light and peace and joy which had united us and transfused us together, suddenly evaporated. Startled, I looked up to see Miss Welly standing outside the car window.

"Good afterNOON Father Hammond," she said icily, completely ignoring me, and before he could reply, she turned and stomped off down the lane; her vast grey cape billowing indignantly out behind her.

I looked at Stephen and knew that the moment had passed, that moment when I really believed that I had come to the end of my quest, found the answer which I had been so earnestly seeking to suffering, to the meaning of life, as I reached out to Him who is life. Miss Welly's angry, disapproving look had sullied everything.

I groped for the handle of the car door and stumbled out into the lane but he was there before me.

"I'm sorry," I gulped. "I'm sorry but I have to go or I'll be late on duty."

Stephen nodded. He understood what I was thinking and didn't try to insist. Like me, he knew just what had gone through Miss Welly's mind.

As I ran through the hospital gate I turned.

He was still standing by the car door where I had left him, a look of utter bewilderment on his face, one hand running distractedly through his dark hair: and I knew that that tell-tale muscle was once again working in his cheek.

CHAPTER TWENTY TWO

Parting

The next day, as we stood in front of Sister's desk to report before going to lunch, the telephone rang. Sheridan went to answer it and then came over and whispered something in the Charge Nurse's ear.

"That was a call from Miss Plumb," the Charge Nurse said, looking at me. "Miss Welly wants to see you in her office as soon as you go off duty."

"Whatever for?" I enquired.

"I've no idea," she replied, shrugging her shoulders. "Miss Plumb just said to tell you to report, isn't that right nurse?"

Sheridan nodded.

As soon as we left the ward I hurried over to the office. Miss Plumb was busily bashing the daylights out of an ancient typewriter. She looked up as I came in.

"Miss Welly is at lunch," she said primly, her thin pale lips barely moving as she spoke. "Come back at half past one."

I left and went over to the dining room, thinking I might as well have lunch too.

When I presented myself at the office bang on the dot of half past one Miss Welly was sitting, unsmiling, behind her impeccably tidy desk. She did not invite me to sit down.

"You are being returned to London tomorrow, nurse," she said as if I were an unwanted parcel, "to go on night duty. Catch the eleven-thirty bus to the station and take the midday train up to town: Miss Balfour is expecting you at the night nurses' home by four o'clock."

I opened my mouth, but not even a gasp escaped. I felt as if I had suddenly been dropped from a great height and all breath had been knocked out of my body.

"That will be all, nurse," she said coldly, and drawing a

blank piece of headed notepaper towards her she took up her pen and began covering it with her thin, spidery writing.

I staggered over to the nurses' home, my head spinning and my mind in a whirl. I couldn't believe what I had just heard and suddenly I knew that I didn't want to go. After all the turmoil I had gone through when I learned that I was being sent to the Annexe I had, in the end, enjoyed it and now that I was working on the Children's Ward I had grown very attached to them all. The idea of uprooting myself and going on alone, without the company of a mass move, to something fresh, was more than I could take at that moment.

A lump rose in my throat as I thought of little Billie, of Douglas hurtling through the ward like a boledo to butt me roughly in the stomach each time I went back on duty, of Patsy, of David and baby Marlene, who was gradually coming back to life and starting to smile. And suddenly, the bewilderment and the pain were replaced by a burning anger.

I flung myself into my room and threw my cloak angrily down on the bed.

'That's IT,' I muttered indignantly. "I WON'T be pushed around like an old broom. I'll... I'll resign."

Then, just as suddenly, I came to my senses.

Resign? Go back to all those kind, loving people who had told me I was crazy, that I was making a dreadful mistake, that I wouldn't last the year? Go back with my tail between my legs and admit that they were right after all? And as these thoughts tumbled through my mind a fighting spirit rose up in me and I knew I couldn't do it, my pride wouldn't let me. I HAD lasted the year and I'd go on to the end.

Ogilvie's head appeared round the curtain.

"What on earth are you making all that racket about?" she asked.

I smiled.

"Sorry," I said. "Were you having a snooze?"

"No, I was just changing my apron before going back on duty."

She sat down on the bed smiling broadly.

"You should have been with us today, you'd have HOWLED: we were rushed off our feet and short of beds and Sister suggested to Doris that perhaps she was well enough to go back home."

Ogilvie burst into helpless giggles.

"Poor old biddie, wish you could have seen her, the performance she put on was worthy of Sarah Bernhardt."

She cast her eyes up to the ceiling in a dramatic gesture.

"Had one of her TURNS."

"Did it work?" I enquired.

"You bet," Ogilvie sparkled. "I think Sister would have held out – she knows Doris from of old and was not impressed – but the RAP was in the ward and he gave in when Doris went rigid and cross-eyed and blue in the face, practically foaming at the mouth. Don't know HOW she does it."

"Is she all right now?" I asked.

"Oh, she was all right the minute the RAP said she could stay," Ogilvie laughed. "Sitting up in bed eating an ENORMOUS lunch ten minutes afterwards as it happens. By the way, how long are you staying next door?"

As she said it I suddenly remembered, but I didn't want to tell her: I wasn't sure whether anger or tears would get the upper hand if I began.

"Not much longer," I said truthfully.

"Oh good," she said. "We miss you."

She caught sight of my bedside clock and bounced swiftly off the bed.

"Glory, do you see the time? I must FLY."

My eyes followed hers to the clock and I saw the books which I had so recently borrowed piled up on the locker beside it.

"Pippa," I called after her, "can I borrow your bike?"

"Help yourself," she called back, as she ran through the swing door.

Picking up the books I put them in a bag and, not even bothering to change, donned my outdoor uniform and went to collect the bicycle. There was a sleepy hush over everything and the whole hospital appeared deserted as I cycled through the gate and out into the lane. When I propped the bicycle against the railings outside Stephen's house I don't know whether I hoped he would be there or not, but as I knocked on his study door and heard his deep voice call out "Come in", for one wild moment I considered dumping the books on the doorstep and running. His voice had sent a shiver of something which I couldn't define, a subtle mixture of pain and delight, of exquisite joy, racing through me. And that same strange fear gripped me again.

"Hallo," he said, getting up from behind his desk as I walked in. "This IS a pleasant surprise. Let me take your coat."

"I can't stay," I said. "I've just come to return your books."

He raised his eyebrows enquiringly.

"Have you read them ALREADY?" he asked.

"Not all of them," I replied, "but I'm leaving and I don't want to go without giving them back to you."

He sat down abruptly on the arm of his old club chair, looking puzzled.

"LEAVING?" he queried. "I don't understand. What do you mean?"

I looked down at the carpet; the tears were not very far from the surface and I didn't want a repetition of yesterday.

"I've been told that I'm to return to London to go on night duty."

"When?"

"Tomorrow."

"TOMORROW!"

I nodded.

He came over and pushed me gently into the opposite armchair.

"Let me take your hat and coat anyway," he said tightly. As he turned to place them on a chair he said grimly, without looking round, "Miss Welly?"

"'Fraid so."

He walked to the window and stood looking out.

"I'm going to miss you," he said quietly at last.

"Oh," I replied, "you hardly know me."

He turned round and looked straight at me.

"I feel as if I've always known you," he answered.

I avoided his gaze and pressed my lips tightly together; those tears were struggling to come through again.

"In fact I can no longer imagine the hospital without you. Ever since the night Audrey Forrest died, .each time I've gone there I've hoped I'd bump into you, but we only ever met in the ward or in a crowd until that day I saw you walking along the lane."

He paused and took a deep breath, his eyes once again gazing through the window at the deserted street.

"I didn't realise what was happening to me until it was too late."

He laughed tersely, without humour.

"And I'm the priest who advises other people how to run their lives."

Turning round he walked back to his old armchair and sat down heavily.

"How different things would have been if my mother had brought me up an Anglican like my father," he said quietly.

I sat staring into the fire.

"Do you wish you were an Anglican?" I asked at last.

"At this moment, yes," he said softly, almost as if he were speaking to himself. "I'd be able to hold your hand without feeling guilty."

He looked across at me and smiled.

"Life's a rum old business, isn't it?"

"I suppose it's what one makes of it."

"That's what I always thought," he said as he got up and went back to gazing out of the window. "Now it seems that life sometimes makes itself."

"Perhaps," he went on reflectively after a few minutes, "there comes a time in every priest's life when he thinks he's made a terrible mistake."

He paused, and I said nothing.

"I suppose he either gets over it and goes on to become a better priest, better able to understand what other people are going through or... he goes under."

"You're not going to go under," I broke in, "you've taken

vows."

He turned and faced me.

"I've taken vows made by MEN," he said quietly, "not by God. The Bible says that God did not think it good for man to be alone, that's why He created Eve to be Adam's companion and helpmate."

I saw that muscle working in his cheek again.

"Over the centuries men have forgotten that and made other rules, rules which are sometimes almost impossible to keep."

"But you're not going to go back on your vows?" I cried, startled at the turn events were taking.

He ran his hand distractedly through his thick dark hair.

"I don't think that any priest who does that ever finds lasting happiness," he said slowly. "He not only destroys himself but he destroys the person he broke his vows for."

He paused and looked across at me.

"The person he loves," he ended, his voice hardly above a whisper. "But I didn't realise until this moment just how hard it is."

My mind went back to the mid-September evening in Jane's room and I heard her voice saying: "Pacts are easy to make, but when it comes to the reality... they are not so easy to keep."

I got up.

"I have to go," I said. "I'm on duty again at half past five and I've got all my packing to do."

"I'll drive you back to the hospital," he said.

"No, it's all right, I came by bike."

"Oh, blast the bike," he exploded. "I'll put it in the boot."

"No," I pleaded, almost in tears again, "please don't. Please, just let me cycle back, otherwise Miss Welly will have something more to cackle about."

I saw the muscle in his cheek tighten.

"If you wish," he said, and he helped me on with my coat.

As he put the bicycle into an upright position for me to mount he asked, "When are you leaving tomorrow?"

"Got to catch the lunchtime train."

I looked up at him wanting to say something, not wanting

to part like this, but no words came, only a great lump in the back of my throat, and I compressed my lips to hold back the tears.

"Thank you for everything," I mumbled, and letting go of the brake, cycled furiously down the road without a backward glance, the tears, now released, flowing freely down my cheeks.

CHAPTER TWENTY THREE

God Be With You

I didn't tell anyone that I was leaving. I just couldn't face the questions: but Home Sister was there as I stuffed the final odds and ends into my suitcase and slammed down the lid of my trunk, which was going up to London in one of the hospital vans later in the day.

"I'll help you carry your case to the bus," she said kindly as I left my little cubicle, and we walked together through the maze of huts and into the lane.

"Goodbye nurse," she said, her homely face warm and compassionate, as the bus creaked to a standstill. "Good luck: stick it out, we all have our little dramas during training but the important thing is not to give in. Here's a few goodies for the journey." And she pressed a crumpled brown paper bag into my hand.

She nodded her head and smiled again as I climbed into the bus and then stood waving her arm vigorously, watching it jolt off down the lane. I wondered just what she had been told.

By the time we reached the station yard I was the last passenger left; all the others had got off at the entrance to the town shopping centre.

As the driver handed my suitcase down to me a tall figure walked out from under the station porch and took it out of my hand.

I looked round, startled. It was Stephen.

Without a word, he took my arm and steered me towards the entrance.

Normally the bus arrived with a good ten minutes to spare but that day it was late and as we approached the platform, still without a word having passed between us, the London train drew in. Opening a carriage door Stephen ushered me in and then climbed in after me and lifted my suitcase onto the rack. As the whistle blew he turned to face me and I saw that muscle working again in his cheek.

"You're a wonderful girl," he said softly, "and oh, how I'm going to miss you."

The whistle blew again and drawing me to him he bent down and gently kissed my lips: but as he did so I could feel the suppressed passion behind his embrace. It was not an affectionate kiss between friends but a kiss exchanged between a man and a woman: a man and a woman who were saying goodbye.

The train slowly began to move away from the station and, releasing me, he jumped down. I pulled blindly at the leather sash and leant out of the window.

"God be with you," he said, taking my hand and running a few yards along the platform. Then the train gathered speed and he let go of my hand and stood there, his arm raised, the wind blowing through his thick dark hair, a look more of bewilderment than of pain on his upturned face.

I flopped back onto the seat and closed my eyes, the tears pouring down my cheeks, and all kinds of dammed up emotions flooded hotly through me. I felt lost, bewildered, broken; I no longer knew what I wanted or what I believed. I looked without interest into the bag which Gert had given me and saw her precious ration of chocolate, and the tears began to flow again.

But the rhythmic clackety-clack of the train's wheels and the dull monotony of the winter landscape flying endlessly by the window had their soporific effect on me and I fell into a heavy dreamless sleep, only to awake as the train drew into Waterloo Station.

Wearily dragging my heavy suitcase down from the rack, I ruminated on how different real life is from that which is portrayed on the silver screen. There had been no impassioned declarations, no wild unleashed emotion, nothing that anyone would have noticed as being out of the ordinary, and the only time the word love had passed between us was when Stephen spoke of the impossibility of breaking his vows.

It had all happened so quickly, only a few short months. But then, I recalled ruefully, it had all happened so quickly to me once before, but that had been in wartime when everything was accelerated: yet the pain had been deep and real and lasting all the same. And I remembered again Jane's words on that memorable September evening:

'It's bad enough to lose someone you love in a war, but when it happens in peacetime...'

I wondered whether this was how life was always going to be for me, happiness just forever eluding my grasp, and I longed to see Jane again, to talk with her in the easy intimacy which we had grown into before I left for the Annexe.

Walking along the dreary platform it struck me that it was little more than a year since we had waved goodbye to my brother from this very station, and it occurred to me that perhaps my mother had felt then as I was feeling now, emptied, desolate. She had just watched the train taking her only son on the first leg of his journey half across the world draw away: she didn't know whether she would ever see him again, and yet she had said nothing.

Remembering this, I realised how little we ever really know not only about what goes on in the hearts and minds of those whose lives cross our paths, but in the hearts and minds of those we love. And once again everything was put on hold. That revelation, that certainty, which I had almost had only two short days before, vanished; and doubt and fear once again installed themselves in their place.

If only I was going on day duty, back to the security and friends I had left last September. But they were living south of the river and the night nurses' home was north, so it would be almost impossible to have any contact outside the hospital. Longingly I thought once again of Jane, of Rachel and of Bunty and I sighed as I walked under the arch and out of the station towards the taxi rank: now I was going to have to begin all over again.

When the taxi drew up in front of the night nurses' home I wondered grimly what horror would be in charge here, but when the door of the old Regency house in the quiet

London square opened, I had a pleasant surprise. Home Sister was small, slim and neat, with a warm welcoming smile. She stood aside to let me in and I realised that she must once have been a very pretty woman.

"Come in, nurse," she said pleasantly. "Leave your case there in the hall. I've prepared tea for us in my room. I thought you'd be ready for some after the journey."

And she ushered me into a pretty chintzy feminine sitting room, with a large bay window looking out onto the bare trees in the middle of the square.

"Take off your coat and sit by the fire."

Pulling a trolley towards her she sat down opposite me. Tea was laid on a dainty embroidered cloth, and there was the comforting smell of hot toast.

I had had no idea how I would be received, nor what Miss Welly might have said about my sudden transfer, but whatever she had been told, Miss Balfour had obviously decided to form her own opinion of me.

The house was very quiet and still as we sat together chatting amiably, crunching the hot buttered toast and sipping the comforting tea.

"Everyone is asleep," Home Sister remarked. "We have a rule that all nurses going on duty that night must be in their rooms by eleven."

I looked up surprised, a sudden wave of dreadful fatigue sweeping over me. It was five past four and I had gathered that I would be expected to go on duty that evening but her words had given me a glimmer of hope: perhaps I was reprieved and would be allowed just one more night to sleep off my exhaustion.

"Except for those returning from their days off," she explained, dashing my hopes with one harsh blow. "Then they don't have to be back till half past four."

She looked at the little gold French clock ticking softly on the mantlepiece.

"Nurse Mead, who is sharing with you, should be back any minute."

I groaned inwardly, wondering if sharing was all part of my punishment and my great age was no longer on my side.

"I'll show you to your room," she said, putting down her cup and pushing aside the trolley, "then I'd advise you to get some sleep."

I looked at her in surprise.

"You'll get through this first night better if you undress completely and go to bed for a few hours," she explained as I picked up my suitcase and followed her up the wide oak-panelled staircase.

She dropped her voice as we walked along the landing past closed doors behind which the night nurses were sleeping.

"Here we are," she whispered, pushing open the door. She walked across to the window, which looked out across the square, and closed the curtains.

"There," she said softly, clicking the bedside lights on and patting the bed farthest away from the door, "I've had this one made up for you. Just unpack what you need and then try to sleep, you can do the rest in the morning. Goodnight nurse, sleep well."

And she tiptoed from the room.

Following Miss Balfour's advice I unpacked what I needed, spread my uniform out on a chair ready for duty and was just padding round in my nightie wondering where on earth I'd put the book I'd taken to read in the train, when the door opened softly and a girl with short chestnut curls and a bright smiling face crept into the room.

"Oh," she exclaimed, "so you're not asleep. Nice to see you."

"Judy," I cried delightedly.

Our paths hadn't crossed since she and Donaldson had shared the desk in front of Bunty and me during those carefree PTS days, which now seemed a lifetime away.

"Sister told me you were going to share with me when I got back," she smiled. "It was a lovely surprise."

I smiled ruefully.

"I hope you really mean that," I said.

"Yes, I do," she replied.

I sat down on my bed and smiled across at her.

"When Sister said Nurse Mead it didn't immediately

register," I tapped my forehead meaningly. "But I'm SO glad it's you; I was dreading meeting whatever monster I might have to put up with snoring in the bed beside me."

Judy smiled back at me as, suppressing a yawn, I crawled into bed, suddenly limp with tiredness and no longer interested in the book, which I concluded I must have left on the train.

"Never realised that one could actually ENJOY going to bed at half past four in the afternoon," I said, yawning again.

"Just you wait till you've done your twelve nights on duty," Judy said, pulling back the blankets and flopping into the bed next to mine. "You'll drop off ANY time, ANYWHERE."

But her voice seemed to be coming from a long way away: the events of the past forty-eight hours had completely robbed me of all my energy and I was already almost asleep.

CHAPTER TWENTY FOUR

Whose Teeth are These?

The bell tore through the peace of that beautiful old house at precisely seven fifteen, bringing me out of a deep sleep. I blinked myself awake and turning over, looked across at the next bed. Judy was sitting up reading and she smiled at me fumbling for my watch.

"It's a quarter past seven," she said. "Feeling ready for the fray?"

I grimaced.

"I'd rather just go on sleeping," I yawned.

Judy placed her book on the bedside locker and kicked off the bedclothes.

"You'll soon get used to it," she laughed.

As I was attempting to plough through the steak and kidney pudding which was already beginning to sit heavily on my digestive system, a Night Ass. came into the hospital dining room and, ringing a bell for silence, began to read out any changes or additions which had been made to the night's work list. I groaned inwardly when I learned that I had not been appointed to a ward, but was to be a 'jobber'.

The girl sitting opposite me made a face.

"You too?" she enquired.

I nodded.

Nobody liked being a jobber: we were sent from ward to ward wherever there was a shortage of staff or an emergency, sometimes working on as many as three or four wards in one night and invariably inheriting all the dirty jobs. It was always the jobber who helped with 'last offices' when the ward was short-staffed.

"Wonder how many they've killed off for us tonight," she said grimly as we left the table.

I was sent to a busy casualty ward where one nurse was in

the sick wing having ripped a muscle in her back and the three remaining were attempting to cope with a sudden flow of accidents.

When I saw the screens closed ominously round a bed I knew what awaited me.

"He's all ready nurse," the Night Ass. said. "The day staff did the first part, you and Nurse Erskine can carry on."

Erskine came over to me wheeling a trolley and we slid aside a corner of the screen and crept inside.

An inert body lay under the sheet. Erskine removed the pillowcase covering his face, and seeing it in the eerie blue light above the bed which was all we had to work by I had a shock. The young man could not have been more than thirty, and his face was bruised and bloodied and set in an expression of absolute terror.

I looked across the bed enquiringly at Erskine, who had been there for the report and must know what had happened.

"He threw himself from a fourth-floor window," she whispered. "Awful, isn't it."

We both sighed, wondering how on earth we were going to make him presentable, so that the relatives would not carry for ever with them this picture of anguish which was now frozen on his face. It was the first time I had worked on a casualty ward and been faced with the task of performing last offices on a body I had not known in life. It felt poignant and yet strangely impersonal.

We worked quickly and silently, neither of us very inclined to talk, merely signalling with a nod of the head or an imperceptible whisper what each wanted the other to pass or to do.

When we had finished the ward was quiet, as quiet that is as any London casualty ward is on a Saturday night. As we gently closed the screens behind us, having done the best we could for the unfortunate young man, a policeman came forward and spoke to the Night Ass.

"What's he want?" I whispered to Erskine.

"The police are always called in for a suicide," she whispered back. "It's a criminal offence: I suppose he'd been sitting by his bedside till he died, hoping to take a statement and make a charge."

I recoiled in horror. It all seemed so terrible, so inhuman: that young man must have suffered enough yet, had he lived, he would have been called upon to face a court.

"Perhaps," I thought grimly, "it's as well he didn't."

As these thoughts went through my mind I remembered Stephen's words: 'All suffering is from the devil. God doesn't make us suffer, He loves us, but sometimes we make ourselves suffer.' And a great longing to see him, to hear his voice again, swept over me as I wondered what had been the reason in this young man's case. Had the devil made him suffer, or had he been responsible for his own suffering? I realised that we would never know, but I felt the old anger rise up inside me once again, that anger which I had abandoned, that luxury of asking questions which I had been prepared to surrender when I told Stephen in the lane outside the hospital just two days before that I wanted to know his Jesus, I wanted Him to come into my life: that precious moment which Miss Welly had spoiled. And the words 'What would have happened if she hadn't come along?' rose tantalisingly into my mind.

"I wouldn't be here now, that's for sure," I said grimly to myself as I walked wearily across to the desk to ask for further instructions.

The night was hectic but at about half past two, when my legs felt like lumps of lead and were beginning to refuse to obey my orders, the Night Ass. came over to where I was checking a drip and told me to go for my off duty.

I looked at her in amazement. I had no idea where to go.

"Put your feet up in Sister's room," she said. "You'll find a blanket on the armchair; light the gas fire and have a snooze, but DON'T undress in any way nor even take off your shoes just in case we have to call you in a hurry."

"How shall I know when to come back?" I enquired.

"Erskine will call you at four," she said, "when it's her turn."

I staggered into Sister's room and didn't even bother to

look for the matches to light the gas fire. I was so exhausted I just collapsed into the armchair, and snuggling the blanket round me immediately fell into a deep sleep. It seemed to me that I had hardly closed my eyes when I felt someone shaking my shoulder and, looking blearily up, saw Erskine standing over me with a cup of tea in her hand.

"Brrrr," she said, rubbing her bare arms, "it's jolly cold in here. Why didn't you light the fire?"

She put the cup down on the table beside me and picking up a box of matches, stooped and held one to the bars. There was an immediate leap of flame and a comforting hissing as the heat sprang out from behind the putty-coloured sticks.

"Gulp that down," she said, turning round and jerking her head in the direction of the steaming cup. "It'll help you get through the rest of the night. Then hand over that blanket, I can't wait to get into it."

I staggered off the chair, feeling cramped and stiff, and handed her the blanket.

"What's the time?" I asked, stretching as I adjusted my cap in the small mirror hanging on the wall. It had perched itself over one eye and I looked as if I were drunk.

"Just four," she answered sleepily, snuggling deeper into the blanket.

"So you didn't have an emergency?"

"Nearly," she yawned, "nasty accident brought in about three."

Her eyes closed.

"Better go," she slurred, "they're awfully busy out there."

And before I had got my aching limbs moving again she was fast asleep.

I shut the door quietly behind me and tiptoed back into the ward. The Night Ass. came over to me and I vaguely wondered when she had her off duty, but only learned much later on when I myself was a fourth-year nurse that the responsibility of a busy ward at night weighed so heavily that one was rarely able to take the weight off one's feet.

At a quarter past six suddenly the ward door swung open, the lights clicked on and two convalescent policemen in slippers and dressing gowns came in pushing a tea trolley.

"Up you get," they shouted, "rise and shine you lazy landlubbers. Come on now, sit up, cuppa char."

And, relieving us of one of our routine early morning tasks, they went from bed to bed handing out brimming cups of the strong orange brew.

I had just been given the list of patients I was expected to wash and prepare for the day before Sister's triumphal entry at eight o'clock and I scurried to the sluice to collect all the paraphernalia needed. As I filled a bowl with hot water I looked through the window; the night was almost over, and although it was still dark outside the beginnings of a fiery dawn were creeping up on the horizon, turning London's dim skyline a deep orange red: it was like a beautiful painting by one of the Old Masters and I stood there breathless, idly dreaming, watching as the dome of St. Paul's became slowly visible and detached itself from the other landmarks which were gradually being etched into place by the winter sun.

There was a sudden interruption and the Night Ass. bustled in.

"Do get a move on, nurse," she said tartly. "You'll NEVER be finished otherwise."

And she bustled out again, deftly holding a bowl in one hand, a kidney porringer in the other and balancing soap, towel and toothmug somewhere in between. I grabbed my bowl and hurried after her to begin scurrying round with the rest, hissing dramatically to each other as our paths hastily crossed on our way to and from the sluice that we would NEVER be ready on time.

At last the day staff came on duty and we all sighed thankfully at the sight of reinforcements. But just as the ward was beginning to look less like an untidy dormitory and more like the spruced up spit and polished barrack room which was its normal daytime face, there was a terrible shriek from the sluice and a harassed probationer came rushing out with a large bowl in her hands.

"Whatever is it nurse?" the Night Ass. said exasperatedly.

"Look," the probationer wailed.

The Night Ass. looked inside the bowl and visibly paled: we were all pale with fatigue by this time but she went positively ghostlike.

"Oh NO," she moaned and grabbed hold of one of the day staff who was hurrying by.

"Who did the sluice last night?"

The nurse looked blank.

"I don't know. Why?"

"Look," the Night Ass. said in her turn, thrusting the offending bowl under her nose.

It was the day nurse's turn to go pale as she gasped in horror.

"It must have been the PTS who has just arrived," she moaned.

"It doesn't matter now WHO it was," the Night Ass. said irritably, "what we've got to do is sort this lot out before Sister arrives."

"But HOW?" the now demented day nurse wailed.

"I don't know," the Night Ass. replied grimly, "but DO something and do it QUICK, she'll be here in ten minutes," and she thrust the bowl into Erskine's hands.

I peeped in and gasped in horror too.

It was FULL of false teeth.

The PTS nurse had obviously been told to collect and clean them for the patients before going off duty, but nobody had thought to explain that each set was to be put in a mug marked with the patient's name. Now we were faced with the impossible task of matching a dozen sets of teeth up with their owners.

"Heavens," I said, barely suppressing a giggle, "how on earth are we going to sort out this lot?"

"I dunno," Erskine mumbled, "let's just go from bed to bed and ask them which set is theirs."

I looked at her in amazement and cast my eyes up to the ceiling.

"Some hopes," I said drily, as we began our round.

The men took it well, though one said he'd forego a fitting and just get himself another set when he went out; in the meantime he'd live on soup! The others peered interestedly into the bowl and tried on a few sets, mostly without any luck, but when we snatched the bowl away and pushed it out of sight at one minute to eight there were still quite a few sitting up in bed with bewildered expressions on their faces, wearing dentures which obviously had never been made for them.

"You're jolly lucky," Erskine said when we finally went off duty and down to the dining room for breakfast, "you're a jobber and the chances are you won't be on the ward tonight. WE'RE the ones who are going to have to take the can back for this whopper."

She giggled.

"Did you see that funny little old barrow boy in the end bed? He chose a gorgeous set of pearlies which certainly didn't belong to him and immediately shoved them under his pillow in case we asked for them back. I suppose he'll pawn them when he gets out and claim a new set on the National Health."

The powdered scrambled egg had never been more welcome nor tasted so good and, ravenous as we were, we consumed mountains of toast before going off to catch the bus back to the nurses' home. But, just as I was about to board it, I suddenly felt I couldn't go back. The thought of being part of the jolly hockeysticks atmosphere, resurrecting and dissecting the night's traumas on the various wards as we sipped cocoa before lights out, was too much to face, and I turned away and started to walk. The night had been hectic and I was tired out, but in spite of the amusing diversion over the teeth, my heart was as heavy as when I went on duty.

I had no idea where I was going, I just kept on walking blindly. Passing a telephone box I had a sudden overwhelming longing to hear Stephen's voice again and, almost without realising what I was doing, I pushed open the door and walked in, fished some coins out of my pocket and dialled his number.

Hearing the steady dring dring at the other end of the line my heart suddenly leapt into my throat and began to beat uncontrollably: there was a click and the beat in my throat was so strong I felt I was going to choke.

"St. Cecilia's Church," I heard him say, "Father Hammond speaking."

I remained there rooted to the spot unable to utter a word.

"Hallo," he said.

But still no words came.

"Press button A, caller," he said patiently, and waited again.

I felt as if I were suffocating, as if invisible hands were clutching my neck and forcing the breath out of me, preventing me from saying one word: and after another pause I heard the click as he put back the receiver.

Then my heart dropped like a stone, falling heavily back into place in my chest. The murderous hands slowly released their hold on my throat and, pushing open the door, I stumbled blindly back into the deserted street.

As I did so, a sudden gust of wind lifted my cap and I realised that I was wandering aimlessly around the streets of London in my indoor uniform; something which was strictly forbidden. But at that moment I didn't really care.

A rag and bone van rattled to a stop beside me and the driver leaned out of his cabin.

"Where ya goin' nurse?" he enquired.

I looked vacantly up at him, but didn't reply.

"Missed the bus back, 'ave yer?"

He leaned over and opened the side door.

"'Op in," he grinned.

Without even stopping to consider what a rag and bone man might be doing trundling round the streets of London on a Sunday morning, I climbed up into the grimy cabin and sat down beside him.

"Chelsea is it?" he asked.

"No," I heard myself saying. "I'm on night duty," and I gave the address of the night nurses' home.

"But perhaps that isn't on your way?" I said anxiously.

"Dun matter," he replied. "I can do a bittova detour – he pronounced it day tour – for you. Me dad was in your 'orspital when 'e fell off a scaffolding: they saved 'is life. I was only a nipper at the time but I'll never forget it: me ma said you nurses was wonderful, angels she called you. Anyfink I can do to 'elp any of you now I do it."

I looked across at him gratefully.

"You'll find most of us chaps 'll give ya a lift when we sees yer walking," he went on. "You just started then?"

"No," I said, "but I've just come up from the country, and we didn't have to catch buses there, everything was on the spot."

"You'll find it diff'rent 'ere," he went on. "They've billeted ya all over London 'aven't they? In the old days all the nurses was living in the 'orspital "

"That was before it was bombed," I smiled.

"Blasted Jerries," he swore and we sat in a companionable silence as he rattled through the almost deserted streets.

"There y'are," he said pulling up at the entrance to the square. "Mind if I leave ya 'ere? If I go into the square I'll 'ave an 'eck of a job to get back out on to the main road."

"Oh no," I said hurriedly, "not at all. It's so kind of you to have brought me this far."

He leaned across me and opened the door.

"It's nuffink," he replied with a cheery wave. "Any toime."

I walked along the square and up the steps into the house. I had no idea what time it was, though the clanging church bells told me that it couldn't be far off eleven, but I couldn't be bothered to reach into my pocket for my large old-fashioned pocket watch and find out.

Sister was hovering in the hall as I went in.

"You look SO tired nurse," she said kindly. "Have you had a very busy night?"

I nodded, and her eyes narrowed. I saw her looking at the black streaks from the lorry's dirty cabin which were all over my apron, but she made no comment.

"Let me make you some cocoa," she fussed, "it will help you sleep."

I smiled at her over the knob of the bannister.

"I don't think I'll need any help."

"Go on to bed then," she said quietly. "Goodnight and sleep well."

I climbed wearily up the stairs but as I reached the top I heard music coming from a radio playing softly in someone's room and suddenly Kathleen Ferrier's lovely rich contralto tones came over the waves.

"What is life to me without thee?" she sang, her voice poignant as if throbbing with pain.

I stood transfixed, tears rising not behind my eyes but into my throat; then from the hall downstairs a clock began to strike. When it reached eleven it stopped and the music stopped with it as the wireless was turned off and its owner settled down to sleep.

I groped blindly along the landing and crept into the room, not wanting to disturb Judy. She had drawn the curtains leaving it shrouded in a dim grey light, and feeling my way I almost tripped over her outstretched feet: she was kneeling beside her bed, hands clasped loosely in front of her, her face uplifted, her eyes closed and her lips moving silently in prayer.

As I tugged at the studs holding my stiff collar in place Judy opened her eyes and climbed into bed.

"Do put the light on," she said.

"Oh Judy," I blurted out, turning round, "I'm SO sorry, I didn't mean to disturb you."

"You didn't disturb me," she smiled. "But I was beginning to wonder what had happened to you: you weren't on the bus."

"No," I replied, kicking my shoes off my aching feet, "I felt like walking."

She raised her eyebrows enquiringly.

"In your indoor uniform?"

"Yes."

"Good job no one saw you."

I didn't reply and she leaned over to her bedside table and picked up the leather-bound book she had had in her hands when I woke up the night before.

Glancing across at her I saw that she was reading the Bible.

CHAPTER TWENTY FIVE

Hidden Tragedies

If I had to share a room, Judy was the best possible person to have as a room mate. She had a delightful sense of humour and was quiet, gentle and unfailingly good-tempered. She must have noticed my irritation, my grumbling and my bad temper, but she never remarked on it, and for that I was grateful.

I was in a pretty raw state emotionally and my jobber's position at the hospital did nothing to boost my morale. Night after night I dragged myself out of bed wondering what horrors Matron's office had managed to dig up for me this time, once again absorbed in myself and my own problems, forgetting that I was not the only jobber on night duty, that there were others doing equally rootless and distasteful jobs and not making martyrs of themselves in the process.

I withdrew from the company of the other night nurses and either went straight to bed when I returned in the morning or grabbed my outdoor uniform and walked endlessly and aimlessly round the streets of north London. I took little interest and even less pleasure in the welcome signs that spring was on the way, as crocuses poked their heads through the damp earth in the quiet Regency squares which were often bathed in the gentle haze that drifted across the capital in the early morning, suffusing them with an almost ethereal light.

Everything was an effort and a burden and, not surprisingly, I seemed to have got on the wrong side of Night Sister.

She was known as the 'Dragon' and was a strict disciplinarian who demanded very high standards and did not suffer fools gladly: looking back, I must have struck her as a fool incarnate, doing everything grudgingly and rarely smiling.

The long weary nights dragged on and I became even more exhausted, the effort of propelling myself on to whatever ward had been assigned to me almost more than I could bear.

On the eleventh night, just when I was beginning to think that relief would never come, I found myself on Women's Medical, this time for the entire stretch. It had been a quiet night and at about four thirty the Night Ass. decided it was safe for her to take a short rest before the morning battle against time began.

As she went off duty a pathetic moan came from a middle-aged woman in a bed halfway down the ward and I tiptoed over to her side.

"Nurse," she said plaintively, "I can't sleep, haven't closed my eyes all night."

I knew she was exaggerating: her snores had echoed round the ward at intervals.

"It's too late for you to have anything to help you sleep now Mrs. Inglis," I whispered, "but I'll make you a cup of cocoa if you like."

"Oh no," she said peevishly, "with my stomach I can't take cocoa."

She shrugged and sighed loudly.

"I wish you nurses would show more concern for your patients," she whined. "I haven't got a wink of sleep all night, just been lying here. If you'd been doing your job properly you'd have seen that without me having to tell you and I could have had a pill earlier."

She pursed her lips disagreeably.

"It's a pity YOU aren't this side of the blanket," she bleated petulantly.

My lips tightened. I'd have given anything to be her side of the blanket.

"You could have had a sedative earlier on, Mrs. Inglis," I whispered, "but it's no good giving you anything this late, you'd feel awful in the morning. Would you like me to make you a cup of tea?"

"No," she pouted. "It's really too bad. Sister SAID I could have a pill and the doctors ordered it, but you young nurses give yourselves airs and think you know better than people who are TRAINED."

She turned over in a huff, pointedly putting her back to me.

"Oh well," she said nastily, "if you WON'T give me anything."

"Mrs. Inglis," I whispered desperately, "it's not that I won't; I can't give you anything but a hot drink at this time of night."

I looked anxiously round me; the two women on either side of her had both begun to stir in their sleep.

"Please do try to be a little quieter," I murmured, "you're waking up the other patients."

"Now you're accusing me of causing trouble," she wailed, and buried her head in the pillow trying her hardest to cry.

I sighed. There didn't appear to be any way out of this dilemma or any point in continuing the conversation; she had obviously made up her mind to be awkward.

"If you don't want a hot drink I don't think there is anything I can do for you," I said quietly and tiptoed away.

I walked over to where Harvey was busy at the steriliser.

"That WOMAN," I hissed under my breath.

"Oh, she's a pain in the neck," Harvey said without looking round. "The day staff are having an awful time with her, always complaining about something."

"She insists she hasn't slept a wink," I whispered.

"WHAT?" Harvey ejaculated, turning round. "The racket she's been making has probably kept all the others awake: those who are REALLY ill. Take no notice, she's just a thoroughly spoilt woman."

I crept away and when I passed Mrs. Inglis' bed a few minutes later the snores had started up again with even greater force.

Just as the morning rush was beginning to calm down Night Sister walked into the ward and went from bed to bed enquiring after each patient. When she approached Mrs. Inglis I saw her beckon to her to come nearer. Sister walked round to her side and Mrs. Inglis sat up in bed and began a long diatribe.

I didn't think much about it until, just as Sister was leaving the ward, she sent for me.

"Mrs. Inglis tells me that you have been very unpleasant with her," she said tersely.

I opened my mouth in surprise.

"Apparently she hasn't slept all night, you refused her a sedative and then accused her of causing trouble."

I shook my head in disbelief. Technically, except for the sleepless night bit, all Mrs. Inglis had said was true, though distorted.

I opened my mouth again to try to explain.

"Don't excuse yourself nurse," Sister said sharply. "The way you behaved is disgraceful. Mrs. Inglis was prescribed a sedative and yet she was allowed to pass a sleepless night and, as if that wasn't enough, you thoroughly upset her into the bargain."

She took a deep breath and her steely grey eyes looked straight at me.

"If THAT is your attitude towards the patients," she concluded, "then I wonder why you imagine you will be of any use in this profession."

And, before I had time to utter one word, she walked straight-backed from the ward.

As I stood there, utterly bewildered, I looked down the line of beds.

Mrs. Inglis was lying innocently back against her pillows but as her eyes met mine she gave a triumphant smile. I knew that she had witnessed the dressing down I had just received, and suddenly a burning anger boiled up inside me at the injustice of it all.

"Nurse," the Night Ass. said exasperatedly, "don't just STAND there, give Harvey a hand with the injection trolley or we'll NEVER be ready."

"That seems to be the standard phrase," I muttered to myself as I strode over to the steriliser, avoiding Mrs. Inglis' eyes in case the anger should spill over in an uncontrollable outburst.

Harvey looked up enquiringly as she fished porringers out of its steaming depths: my fury must have shown on my face, but she wisely made no comment.

As I left the dining room after breakfast still boiling with anger, I bumped into Judy.

"Coming to the bus?" she asked pleasantly.

"No," I snapped.

She looked taken aback.

"I'm going to see Matron," I stormed. "I've HAD ENOUGH."

Judy caught hold of my arm.

"Bertie," she said anxiously, "you're tired."

(Bertie was the pet name my father had given me when I was very young and it had somehow followed me into training. Quite why he called me this is shrouded in mystery but it was probably because I should have been christened Roberta Deirdre and at the last minute he changed everything and decided to name me 'Little Nora' after my mother. Stephen was the only person who called me Noreen.)

"Don't do anything in a hurry," Judy pleaded. "Come back to the home and simmer down."

She paused and looked straight at me.

"We can talk about whatever it is that is upsetting you, if you like," she ended.

"No," I said, pulling myself away from her grasp, "I've made up my mind, enough is enough."

And I stormed off.

Matron was 'at home' to any nurse who wanted to see her immediately after breakfast every morning: all we had to do was wait in the little corridor outside her office. There were already three or four nurses waiting when I arrived and by the time my turn came I had simmered down slightly.

I hadn't been in Matron's office since the day I went for my interview, almost two years earlier, when she had accepted me for training and welcomed me so graciously to the hospital. As I walked back into the quiet imposing room, she looked up from her desk and smiled, a small immaculate figure in her plain navy blue dress with the trim white collar and cuffs, her iron grey hair swept up into a bun beneath her tall cap.

"Sit down nurse," she said pleasantly. "What can I do for you?"

"I want to resign," I said tensely.

She raised her eyebrows enquiringly, but otherwise didn't seem to be in the least perturbed by my startling statement.

"Is there any particular reason?" she asked calmly.

"I can't take any more," I burst out.

She leaned forward, her hands clasped in front of her on the desk.

"Perhaps nurse," she said quietly, "you had better begin at the beginning and tell me the real reason for this sudden decision."

I looked across at her and tears started to come to my eyes, her kindness dissipating all my anger. Suddenly I didn't know what to say, it all seemed to petty.

"Has anything happened recently, this last night perhaps, to cause you to want to take this drastic step?" she asked gently.

I nodded glumly, and she leaned back in her chair and looked straight at me, her brown eyes kind and compassionate.

"Take your time nurse," she said softly.

"I've had enough of Night Sister," I muttered. "She's been gunning for me ever since I arrived. I don't know why, I can't do a thing right."

I gulped.

"But this morning was TOO much."

Matron nodded encouragingly and the whole story came tumbling out.

"Nurse," she said quietly, when the torrent had ceased, "I DO understand how you feel but you must see things from Sister's point of view as well."

I looked up. It had never occurred to me to see the situation from anyone's point of view but my own.

"Night after night," Matron went on, "she has the tremendous responsibility for every patient in this hospital on her shoulders and when she came to your ward this morning she was at the end of her round and no doubt very tired."

"We're ALL tired," I broke in petulantly, but Matron ignored my interruption.

"Perhaps she'd been dealing with really difficult situations, possibly tragic situations and then to hear this – I agree unfair – story about a nurse who, in her eyes, had been callous to a patient, was probably just too much."

She smiled sweetly at me.

"Had your ward been the first one on her early morning round, things might have been very different."

I didn't look up, still smarting over the injustice.

"Maybe she's getting too old for the job," I said spitefully and looked up surreptitiously to see how this remark would be taken, but Matron didn't react.

"Sister's not as old as you think nurse," she said quietly. "But she's just discovered that she's ill and I'm afraid will no longer be able to continue with active nursing."

I looked up amazed.

"Just imagine what that means to her," Matron went on. "Nursing is her whole life. She's a wonderful nurse, whatever you may think, and now she has been condemned to spending the rest of her working days doing administrative work here in the office. Tomorrow will be her last night on duty."

For a moment there was a silence as all this seeped in, and I began to feel ashamed.

"What is the matter with her?" I whispered, not daring to look up and meet Matron's eyes, fully expecting to hear the dreaded word cancer.

"A nasty bug she picked up in the prison camp, for which there is no lasting cure," she went on. "It has lain dormant for a few years and has now suddenly flared up."

"In the PRISON CAMP?" I gasped. "I didn't know she'd been in a prison camp."

"There's a lot of things you young nurses don't know about the Sisters who appear to be such dragons to you," Matron commented drily. "Many of them finished their training in the late thirties and had rosy dreams for the future: like you they probably all hoped to get married and have children, but many of these had their lives and their hopes shattered by the war."

She turned her clear gaze upon me as I sat there, now cowering and ashamed.

"In this hospital there is many a tragedy hidden beneath a Sister's cap, only you don't necessarily know about it."

She paused but I kept my eyes riveted to the carpet, as waves of remorse poured through me.

"Sister saw her husband killed in front of her eyes when the Japanese invaded Malaya," she continued.

"Her husband?" I gasped. "I didn't know she'd been married."

"As I said, there's a great deal you young nurses don't know," Matron remarked laconically.

"Her husband was the assistant chaplain here when she was in training; a fine young man, I remember him very well. They married as soon as she had qualified and went out to Malaya in the summer of 1938. Sister spent the entire war in a Japanese prison camp where her little son died of malnutrition."

She paused and looked down at her hands.

"He was only two years old," she ended.

My head was spinning.

"I thought that all she had ever known were the four walls of this hospital," I said brokenly. "I never imagined..."

But the end of my sentence trailed away.

"The young can be very cruel," Matron said quietly, "often without meaning to be."

She looked out of the window.

"Sister came back here when the war was over to try to remake her life: she threw herself into her work and gave it every ounce of energy she had."

She sighed.

"And now she has got to give that up."

She turned back and smiled at me.

"So you see," she said gently, "if she's sometimes a little terse, there IS a reason."

I sat in stunned silence thinking of Night Sister, whom I

had imagined to be an 'old maid' knowing nothing of life or the outside world, having no inkling of the terrible tragedy which she concealed behind a mask of efficiency and severity, only now realising that all the time her heart must have been bleeding. And I wondered whether we young probationers had not made her life even more of a misery.

The thought which had struck me as I walked with a heavy heart along the platform at Waterloo Station only two weeks before came back into my mind and I realised once again how little we really know about the people with whom we come into daily contact, and how unkind we can unwittingly be simply because we are unable to see behind the masks they are wearing.

I looked up at Matron and I didn't know what to say.

"Do you still want to resign nurse?" she asked quietly.

I shook my head.

She looked down at her desk and leafed through a pile of papers.

"Let me see now," she pondered, "you've been jobbing ever since you arrived back?"

I nodded.

"That's never very easy. And tonight is your last night before your days off?"

I nodded again, marvelling at her efficiency: she seemed to have the itinerary of the whole hospital at her finger tips.

"Well, I'll have a word with Sister before this evening," she said pleasantly.

"Oh no," I broke in, now thoroughly ashamed of my behaviour, "PLEASE don't do that."

"It's best that we get this cleared up," she said. "She's probably just as upset as you are about it if the truth be told. I'll just mention that I've seen you and I'll arrange for you to go onto a ward permanently when you come back next week."

"Matron," I mumbled, "I'm sorry."

And at that moment I wanted to tell Night Sister that I was sorry too: sorry I'd misjudged her, sorry I'd been so petty, sorry for the pain she was carrying beneath her starched exterior. But I knew that it was not possible and that even if it had been, my pride would never have allowed me to do it. But God is so gracious and many years later, when our paths crossed by chance – was it chance or just His perfect timing? – He was to give me that opportunity.

I looked across at Matron, finally able to meet her eyes, and she smiled at me.

"You're very tired nurse," she said kindly. "That's obvious, and you've missed the bus back."

She picked up her telephone.

"Go to Casualty," she said as she replaced the receiver. "There is an ambulance taking a patient to the National Hospital for tests in fifteen minutes' time: they'll drop you at the nurses' home."

I stood up still feeling desperately sorry for my outburst, and not knowing what to say. But Matron graciously put me at my ease.

"I'm pleased we've had this little talk," she said, getting up from behind her desk, and I was surprised once again by how small she was. I marvelled that such power, such dignity, such hidden strength could be contained in that tiny body. "Don't hesitate to come and see me again if there is anything bothering you."

I bit my lip, the tears not far away.

"Thank you Matron," I gulped, as I moved towards to door.

"Good night nurse," she said kindly, "sleep well." And sitting back down at her desk she picked up her pen.

CHAPTER TWENTY SIX

Job's Story

When I walked into the room Judy was sitting in the armchair in her dressing gown, a Bible open on her lap.

She smiled pleasantly, but didn't ask any questions.

I sat down on my bed and kicked off my shoes, utterly drained.

"I feel the most ghastly hypocrite," I said.

"Why?" Judy enquired, looking up.

"I've just been to see Matron, flounced into her office full of anger and self-pity and she completely deflated me. But in the nicest possible way."

"Do you feel better?" Judy asked.

"I feel a worm," I replied, gazing miserably at my feet.

When I looked up Judy was staring at me intently, as if she too could see right through me, but she didn't make any comment.

"What are you reading?" I asked at last.

She picked the Bible up off her knee.

"Job," she said.

"Isn't that rather miserable?"

"On the contrary," she smiled. "HE wasn't miserable, it was the others who tried to make him so."

"Oh," I said, not really interested. "What's it all about?"

"Suffering," she said simply, and I immediately pricked up my ears.

"It shows how God does not allow us to be tested beyond our powers of endurance. Sometimes He lets the devil have his way with us, but only to prove to Satan that he is a defeated enemy and can never win. It was a test of Job's faith."

She placed the worn leather volume back on her lap.

"Job is one of the oldest books in the Bible," Judy went

on. "It goes back to the time of Abraham, but I find it more meaningful than anything else I've ever read about suffering."

I looked across at her but didn't comment further, the sudden spark of interest which had flared up in me when she mentioned the word 'suffering' slowly dying out. I didn't want to hear a treatise on ancient Hebrew writings, I wanted an explanation; a cut-and-dried explanation: I wanted an answer to my lingering 'why's. And now it didn't seem as if she were going to be able to give me one.

"Wasn't it Job," I asked more out of politeness than anything else, "who lost his home, his family and everything and was comforted by some friends?"

Judy smiled.

"I'd hardly say comforted," she commented. "His so-called friends only added despair to his misery. All THEY could offer in the way of comfort when he asked why these disasters should happen to him – and he asked why fifteen times – was judgement, telling Job that he was paying the price for his sins."

"But didn't the story have a happy ending?" I queried.

"Yes it did," Judy replied quietly, "because after the lengthy discourses of his 'comforters', which only ended in complete deadlock, God spoke to Job, and in a very few words impressed him with His absolute sovereignty. I was only reading about it when you came in. Just listen to this.

" 'Were you there when I made the world? Do you know where the light came from? Who laid the corner stones of the world? Do you know how clouds float in the air?'"

Judy looked intently at me as if she felt that those questions were also intended for me.

"... and Job," she continued, "who had argued endlessly with his friends about his calamities, immediately acknowledged God's supremacy over the universe and bowed down to it."

Her eyes returned to the pages of her Bible.

"'I talked about things I did not understand,' Job replied, 'about marvels too great for me to know. . . But now I have seen you with my own eyes I repent in dust and ashes.'"

She paused and I did not know what to say.

I once again had that queer feeling that she was looking deep into my heart and I shifted uncomfortably, wondering whether she thought I needed to repent in dust and ashes too.

"When God spoke to him," Judy said softly, "Job understood what his faith meant to him; it didn't depend on things going well, it was real."

She smoothed the pages of her Bible absently.

"Like God's love for us," she went on, "it was unconditional. If our faith is to be of any use, it HAS to be unconditional."

One of my sudden flashes of anger flared up inside me.

"But what about Job's questions and the fifteen whys you mentioned?" I asked belligerently, my own whys now looming menacingly on the horizon.

"God didn't answer them directly," Judy replied quietly. "But He answered the needs of Job's heart."

A silence fell in the room, broken only by the echo of a street vendor calling out his wares in the square below.

"Job passed God's greatest test of faith," Judy went on as if collecting together and docketing her thoughts. "The test we are all submitted to when life overwhelms us, when, to quote a psalm, 'the seas roar and rage and the earth is shaken'."

She paused and I could hear the vendor's voice fading into the distance.

"In his darkest moment Job never lost his faith in God."

Her voice dropped almost to a whisper.

"He lost everything else; he went through terrible trials but he never gave in, never denied God, and in the end his faith was rewarded."

She placed the open Bible gently back on her lap.

"That faith which made him say: 'Even though He slay me I will trust in Him'," she ended softly, her eyes far away.

The vendor's voice now had completely disappeared and the silence between us was electric, uncomfortable.

I laughed shortly.

"Wasn't there any other way of proving he had faith?" I

asked sarcastically.

"God doesn't ask us to prove anything," she said quietly. "In fact, He asks very little of us: but sometimes we need to prove to ourselves that our faith is real."

She looked through the window at the trees in the square outside.

"Anyone can have faith when the sun is shining and everything is going well: it's when the shadows and the darkness come that we need to test OURSELVES – not GOD."

Judy turned and looked directly at me once again, but I avoided her eyes.

"I learned that lesson the hard way two years ago when my younger brother was knocked down and killed by a drunken motorist," she said softly.

I shot an agonised glance at her, expecting tears, but her gentle brown eyes were dry, yet warm with compassion, and I looked quickly away. I didn't know what to say.

"Read it sometime," she went on, "and you'll see what I mean. Because Job suffered he was a different person at the end from what he was at the beginning... No one comes through the fires of suffering without being changed."

"Not always for the better," I put in drily, and hated myself for saying so, after what I had just heard.

"That depends on us," Judy answered quickly. "We have a choice. Either we can lean on God in our pain and allow Him to transform us into the person He wants us to be – the person He has always wanted us to be – or we can, as the Bible warns us, lean on our own understanding."

Judy's eyes travelled back to the pale grey patch of sky appearing in the window, a single tear glistening on her cheek. But her face was radiant.

"The Bible tells us," she ended softly, "that if we share Christ's suffering, we shall share His glory."

And leaning back in her chair she picked up her Bible and continued to read.

"Judy," I said hesitantly, after a few minutes, "do you have this faith, this special relationship which I seem to have heard so much about lately?"

She looked up.

"With Jesus?" she queried.

I nodded.

"Yes," she said simply, "I do. I have accepted Him as my personal Saviour and it has made all the difference to my life, especially in the last two years."

There it was again, those words 'my personal Saviour': it seemed I couldn't get away from them and yet I couldn't get near to them either. I had been so close that afternoon in the lane outside the hospital but since then something had tightened round my heart and I didn't want to know. . . Ironically, every time I got anywhere near the truth, got near to knowing Jesus as a real person and not just a cardboard cut-out, a plaster statue, every time the veil was lifted and I was about to glimpse the beauty which all these committed Christians seemed to carry in their mind's eye, the veil suddenly dropped again and what I had thought was finally within my grasp was snatched away from me.

And I wondered if this devil chap had anything to do with it.

I laughed mirthlessly and Judy looked up enquiringly.

"Don't you ever read anything except the Bible?" I asked.

"Of course I do," she smiled. "I'm an avid reader, but I always set aside part of the day for reading my Bible; it's a habit I took when I became a Christian and I've never regretted it. In fact, I don't know how I could get through the day, or night at the moment, without it."

"But isn't it BORING," I enquired, "reading the same old thing time after time?"

"Not in the least," she answered, and she leaned forward earnestly. "You see, the Bible isn't like any other book; I can read the same passages over and over again and each time I get something different, some new insight. It's incredible and wonderful at the same time."

I nodded but didn't comment and, going to the window, stood looking out, aching inside and trying not to think of Stephen.

"Bertie," Judy said gently, "what's the matter?"

For a fraction of a second I hesitated, that overwhelming

desire to hear his voice which had swept over me in the street ten days ago now translating itself into a desire to talk about him, to share what had happened. Judy would understand, she wouldn't judge or condemn me, and impulsively I half turned towards her. Then the remembrance of Miss Welly's disapproving face framed in the car window came back to my mind and I knew that the memory was too precious, too fragile to share with anyone. I couldn't take the risk of something so beautiful being sullied again.

"Oh nothing," I replied absently, leaning my throbbing head against the cold window pane.

"I don't want to poke my nose in where it's not wanted," she continued, "but I had such a shock when I saw you that first day here. You've CHANGED so."

I looked round.

"What do you mean?"

"Oh, I don't know, it's difficult to explain."

She paused.

"When Sister told me you had arrived and were going to share with me I was so pleased, but when I came into the room I couldn't believe you were the same person."

I frowned, not understanding.

"I thought you were just very tired, you looked so pinched and drawn, but it's not only that. Something else has changed, the spark has gone out of you."

I smiled.

"I don't remember there ever having been a very strong one."

"Oh there was," she said. "You were such a lot of fun at PTS, Bertie, I don't know how our set would have survived without you."

Her remark cheered me up slightly and I was pleased by the compliment.

"The Sisters didn't always think so," I replied, "and they still don't."

"Maybe not," she said, "but you were all the same."

She sat quietly waiting and once again I was tempted to tell her all that had happened in the last few weeks, how my life had suddenly been turned upside down and I now found myself in an impossible impasse, a situation to which there was no solution.

I half turned towards her once again, then I remembered that evening in the restaurant when I now realised it had all begun for me and I saw Stephen's face as he stood on that dreary country platform, his hair blowing in the wind, his bewildered expression and I knew that he was as hurt and as vulnerable as I was. I could not indulge in the luxury of sharing with another human being those precious moments, that precious flame which had been lit between us.

Picking up my towel, I walked over to the door.

"Oh, just the end of the year and exams looming up," I said faking a yawn, "and perhaps I need a holiday. We're due for one soon, aren't we?"

Judy nodded her head, but I could see that she wasn't taken in by my remark. She looked straight at me as I turned in the doorway and I had that same uncanny feeling which I had had with Stephen that she could read my thoughts.

"When we're hurt," she said slowly, "it's easy to blame God and blacken His character, because He never answers back, never vindicates or justifies Himself: He doesn't have to."

She leant forward and picked up her Bible, opening it again in the same place.

"Try reading Job," she ended. "You'll see that the experiences of life, whether terrible or just plain monotonous, are unable to change the love of God."

She smiled at me as I stood in the doorway, not knowing what to reply. How did she know that, deep in my heart of hearts, I had been railing against the God I'd almost come to know, holding Him responsible for this new pain which had got a foothold and had now completely invaded my life?

"His love is not built on a passing whim," she said, "but upon a solid rock which nothing can break."

Her eyes dropped back to that Bible and, my mind in a turmoil, I quietly closed the bedroom door and shuffled along to the bathroom.

CHAPTER TWENTY SEVEN

Through it All

It was true that I needed a holiday – we all did.

A year working at that pace, added to the drastic change of lifestyle, had left us very jaded – but beforehand, there were our preliminary exams to cram for and every available minute was spent 'chewing over old bones' as Bunty had once so eloquently put it.

When the results were announced, to my great surprise, I had passed.

I had got through that first year and would now change my black belt for the coveted stiff white one, thereby proclaiming to the world at large that I was someone to be reckoned with, someone who had a certain amount of experience behind her.

Towards the end of March I went up to Scotland to spend the long-awaited holiday with friends. The weather was glorious: day after day the sun shone brilliantly out of a clear blue sky and we picnicked on the deserted shores of frozen lochs, returning relaxed and happy to spend the evenings sitting by a roaring log fire playing endless games of canasta, which had just become the rage.

When I went back to the hospital in April it was with a new enthusiasm and a sense of purpose. I had learned a lot in that first decisive year of my training, that year which determined whether a student nurse would stay the course or not and, although I still had a great deal more to learn in the three years which lay ahead, I was no longer a raw probationer, at everybody's beck and call, gasping and floundering like a fish caught in a net. I would now have responsibilities in this large busy hospital, not only to the patients but also towards the new recruits who had arrived after me.

I had also changed.

Through my first-hand contact with people who were hurting I had acquired a new depth, a deeper sensitivity, but I think that the greatest change was in my attitude towards others. I had become more caring and had learned during those first twelve months, perhaps without even realising it, that every patient was an individual, a person in his or her own right and a being of worth, not only needing devoted and loving care but having a right to it.

As I shed my chrysalis shell and entered my second year, I knew that, even though it was not at the time apparent to me, there was a purpose for my life and somewhere along the way I would find the answer I was seeking. And although there was still a feeling of emptiness and raw pain in my heart, I at last felt that I could cope. Having managed, in spite of everything, to leap the initial barriers of my training, I was able to look the next three years squarely in the face and set my mind to full steam ahead in my professional, if not my emotional, life.

On my return to duty I was sent to work in the Gynaecological Unit which was housed in a small hospital in another part of London. When after three months we all changed again, I found myself back at the main hospital. This time I was in the operating theatre, which I didn't enjoy at all. I much preferred to nurse my patients when they were conscious!

Jane was by now on night duty and when the time came for us to move round once more she was transferred to the Annexe, while I was sent to an ear, nose and throat ward. So although we kept in touch as best we could, with all this boxing and coxing it wasn't until the beginning of our fourth and final year that we actually found ourselves together, both working in the main hospital and once again living in the same nurses' home.

One evening when we were relaxing together in my room, Jane told me that she had met a young doctor who had been sent over from Pretoria to do research at the hospital: they had decided to marry and return to South Africa as soon as she had finished her training.

When she shyly told me of this unexpected happiness which had come into her life she looked at me enquiringly, hoping that I would be able to share something with her. But those last few weeks I had spent at the Annexe were still very vivid in my mind, still very precious, and I felt that were I to share them with anybody the memory might fade and finally disappear. Although at times it was still painful it was gradually turning into a beautiful cameo, something perfect which could never have been.

But Jane's unexpected announcement suddenly brought home to me the fact that this phase in my life, which I had once thought I would never survive, was finally coming to an end: another chapter was closing and another fresh start would soon have to be made.

Although on the day we arrived at the PTS we none of us thought our finals would ever be a reality, suddenly we all realised that the years had rolled by and they were no longer a far distant nightmare but were looming darkly on the horizon. As we began frantically working towards the final goal, panic and hysteria gripped every one of our hearts.

At the height of all this frenzied cramming, Ogilvie dropped an absolute bomb when, to the astonishment of us all, she announced her engagement to Archie Heeley-Walker. As soon as she had taken her exams, they rushed off and had the wedding of the year at one of London's most fashionable churches.

When, after a magnificent fully choral ceremony, they walked back down the aisle as man and wife, to the peal of bells and the crashing chords of the Wedding March thundering out from the organ loft above, followed by a swarm of little pages and bridesmaids, Heeley-Walker was a different man – hardly recognisable in fact, even the teeth seemed to have disappeared. His beautiful, vivacious bride, bubbling at his side and lost in a cloud of tulle and old lace, had quite literally transformed him.

Bunty still hadn't managed to lassoo HER curate, but she decided to nurse for a time in Australia and try her luck there. Donaldson was off to do the same thing in what was then Rhodesia, Judy had applied to do her midwifery in the Gorbals and Rachel, not surprisingly, had become engaged to an eminently suitable young man who did something in the City. Also not surprisingly, Morley-Watson had won the nurses' Gold Medal for efficiency and proficiency, and been offered a charge nurse's post at the hospital to take effect immediately her training ended.

Poor pathetic Braithwaite had not managed to stay the course. During her second year it had all proved too much for her fragile nervous system and she had suffered a serious breakdown. Returning to the hospital afterwards had been out of the question but, mercifully, an unmarried cousin of her mother's had offered her a home and, as far as anyone knew, she had settled down quite happily, spending her days helping with church fêtes and pruning roses in a village in the Cotswolds.

After four years of living together at close quarters, of laughter and tears, of frustrations and satisfactions, of almost impossibly high professional standards being expected of us and a growing devotion to duty, a love and respect for those entrusted into our care regardless of colour, class or social standing, interwoven with the unwavering principle, instilled into us throughout our training, that human life is sacred and human rejects are honoured by God; of coming face to face with suffering in all its aspects and of being bound to the hospital in a love-hate relationship – it was suddenly all over. Our diplomas were in our hands, we had earned our coveted hospital badges. Our loose-knit little group was finally splitting up, with everyone plunging out in different directions: and I simply did not know what to do.

There were endless opportunities open to me.

I could have taken a midwifery or any other specialised course, applied to work in another hospital, joined the Armed Forces as a Nursing Sister or even teamed up with one of my set who was leaving to nurse abroad for a few years. But whatever avenue I explored I seemed to meet with a blank wall, and I did not understand why. I was, in fact, totally bewildered and decided that perhaps the grind of exams had exhausted me and it would be better to wait a while rather than rush into a responsible nursing position immediately. I did not rule out the possibility of returning to it later on: but as it happens I never did.

I now realise that God had other plans for my life. Plans which would have bewildered me even more had He revealed them to me earlier: it would have seemed such a waste of four years' training. Had I then been a committed Christian I think I would have felt secure and at peace resting in the words which God spoke to Jeremiah:

"I know the plans I have for you, plans to prosper you and not to harm you, plans to give you hope and a future."

For He has since shown me that those four years were certainly not wasted and that in the life He was calling me to lead, and which would begin to blossom once I had acknowledged Him as my Saviour, all that I had learned would be invaluable; for there are as many, perhaps even more, sick and suffering people walking the streets needing, aching for loving devoted care as there are in hospital beds. He later revealed to me that if only I would bloom where He had planted me, I could be just as useful to Him as I would have been had I donned a Sister's uniform and taken charge of a hospital ward.

The day I left the hospital for the last time was a Sunday, and as I walked out I felt an elation which was immediately followed by a terrible emptiness as the question 'What now?' loomed darkly in my mind. What DID happen on that final Sunday afternoon was one of those strange coincidences, which I now call God-incidences, which so often occur on our Christian walk.

I was standing on Westminster Bridge looking idly down into the waters which were flowing evenly by underneath, my mind wandering back down the years remembering, oddly enough with a kind of gratitude, all that I had learned during my training. Remembering also how badly I had sometimes hurt, I glanced up and saw someone coming towards me.

The walk was familiar and, as I turned and leant on my elbows against the stone parapet, I recognised a friend I had once worked with at the BBC immediately after the war, and hadn't seen or heard anything of for years.

We stood and looked at each other in amazement.

Liz hadn't changed, though she didn't immediately recognise me in my uniform.

"WHAT a surprise," she said and we both laughed delightedly.

"What are you doing?" she enquired.

"At this minute?"

"Yes."

"Nothing much. I finished my training today and I was just trying to pluck up the courage to go back and pack my trunk, but I needed a breath of fresh air first. Do I stink of lysol?"

"It could be worse," Liz smiled.

I noticed that she had the haunting fragrance of an expensive French perfume clinging to her.

"Let's go and have tea," she suggested, hailing a passing taxi.

"What are you intending to do now?" she asked as we settled into comfortable chairs in the River Room at the Savoy, where I felt slightly conspicuous in my nurse's uniform.

"I've no idea," I replied.

Liz sipped her tea thoughtfully as I slipped a fork effortlessly into a gooey white swan meringue which I had always loved and which, in spite of rationing, the Savoy still managed to serve at tea time.

"Would you be interested in coming to Paris?" she enquired, looking at me intently over the rim of her cup.

I was completely taken by surprise and, for a moment, wondered whether she could be serious.

"Depends what to do," I answered warily.

"Well," she said, putting down her cup and leaning back in her chair as she lit a cigarette, "as it happens I'm running the English side of a French press agency over there: we're expanding, and I'm looking for an assistant. Would it interest you?"

I leaned back too and let out a deep breath, then

laughed at the incongruity of the situation. After working for four years in the slums of London I was now being offered a job in Paris, the world's most beautiful, glamorous city: and I wasn't sure I could cope with such an abrupt transition.

"Do you think I'd be any good?" I demurred. "I've been out of the swim for four years."

"Oh, I've no worry on that score," she replied. "You're practically bilingual and your experience at the BBC would be invaluable."

And she began to outline the job she was offering me.

"I'm returning to Paris tomorrow," she ended, "but I'll be back at the beginning of next week. Think about it and give me your answer then."

"Are you SURE?" I asked. "It's very sudden."

"I'm sure," she smiled.

Liz was ten years older than I and a very capable career woman, used to making quick decisions.

"I wasn't consciously looking for anyone this time over, though I've been making some tentative enquiries, but it seems that Fate put you across my path after all these years."

She leaned forward and stubbed out her cigarette.

"If you're willing to come and give it a try, I think you'd find it interesting."

I wonder what my feelings would have been had God, at that moment, lifted the veil blowing hazily across my future and allowed me a glimpse? Allowed me to see how that "chance" meeting with Liz after all those years would result in my leaving England for good as the door to a completely new life, one I could not then even have imagined, was now opening: a door leading me to another country, another culture, where marriage and motherhood, the blackness of mental depression and the anguish of abortion awaited me. But also, as I have recounted in previous books, after many years of seeking and somehow not finding, to the ultimate joy of finally meeting Jesus, my Living Lord.

CHAPTER TWENTY EIGHT

And the Best was Yet to Come

All of this lay ahead of me on that sunny summer afternoon as I went back to my hospital room, totally bemused and confused by the turn events had taken, and started to pack my trunk for the last time. But, in the middle of it, I suddenly sat down and wrote to Stephen telling him what I now intended to do. We had had very little contact during the intervening three years although I had often had news of him indirectly from nurses who had been working at the Annexe: he was very well loved by staff and patients alike and it wasn't difficult to drop the casual question and discover what was happening to him.

He had written to me the year before to say that he was being moved nearer the coast on the final lap before being given a parish of his own. His letter had been warm yet almost impersonal, but it was not difficult to read between the lines and to realise that, like me, there was still an emptiness in his heart and life which only time could fill. We had both tried to fill it with hard work and, so far, seemed on the surface to have succeeded.

But as I sat at the desk in my cluttered room, which had already taken on an impersonal look as it awaited the next occupant, it was almost as if my future was now settled and out of my hands. By writing to Stephen I was sealing a bargain and ending a chapter.

His reply came back almost immediately.

"Do you remember my telling you in the train that dreary February day that I thought you were a wonderful girl?" he wrote. "Well, I still do and I still miss you very much but if this is what you really believe you'd be happy doing then may God bless you and go with you. I think I want your happiness more than anything in the world, though I hate the thought of your being so far away."

I smiled when I read his words. Paris wasn't so far away. And yet that twenty-two miles of water meant that I was not to see him again for more than ten years and, when I finally did, I was married to Jacques and the mother of two sturdy little blond boys.

I still hadn't met his Jesus who so nearly came into my life that faraway winter afternoon when he wiped away my tears—perhaps because, once the moment has passed, it so often seems easier to ignore that still small voice inside us, to fill the aching void with work and continue merely to pay God lip service, to be His parishioners instead of abandoning all and becoming His child. I don't know. But what I do know is that when Stephen and I did unexpectedly come face to face with each other one early morning back in the hospital where I was now a patient, Jesus was not then very far away.

I see now that He never had been.

Even though in the hustle and bustle of hospital life and, later, amongst the bright lights and the glitter of Paris, I had momentarily lost the vision of Him which had been so clear to me that afternoon in the lane outside the Annexe, God the loving Father had never lost sight of me. He had held me and gently guided me until I came to the end of myself, the end of my long search, and found the shelter of His everlasting arms. And when it finally happened it was so simple, so beautiful, so uncomplicated; the veil was gently lifted once and for all and I saw His face. And I couldn't understand why I had waited so long.

That unexpected meeting with Stephen came at a time when I was raw with pain, having just sacrificed the little daughter I was carrying, and which both Jacques and I longed to have, because medical evidence had pronounced that it was her life or mine.

As we sat together in the cold, empty waiting room Stephen had been gentle and understanding; but he didn't excuse or minimise the dreadful decision I had taken, though he did not judge or condemn me either. He merely took from his pocket his well-worn Bible and read to me the words of Psalm 139, showing me that God knew my baby, loved my baby and that my baby was unique and precious in His sight because He had planned every day of her life before I even knew that I was carrying her.

His words had pierced my heart but at the same time they had cleansed the wound and started my healing. For, having shown me, sadly too late, that abortion, whatever else we like to call it, is murder, and my baby had been murdered by well-meaning people in an antiseptic operating room – not technically by my hands but upon my command because I had signed her death warrant – he then showed me that murder is not the unforgivable sin.(*)

For if Jesus could forgive those who have cruelly murdered Him, as my baby had been cruelly murdered, He could and He would forgive me: more than that He longed to forgive me and relieve me of the heavy burden of guilt which was now weighing me down.

Everyone else had justified my abortion, the doctors, my vicar, kind loving friends: the law was just about to be passed in Britain making it perfectly legal for women in my situation to get rid of their babies.

"But there is God's law and man's law," Stephen had explained, his face tired and strained, that tell-tale muscle working in his cheek. "It depends which law you believe in, which law you want to follow."

He had run his hand thoughtfully through his still thick black hair now lightly flecked with grey, in a gesture which I knew so well.

"Something which is morally wrong," he had ended sadly, "can never be legally or politically right."

His words had cut deeply into my heart on that dull January morning, but I knew that when he had written all those years before that he wanted my happiness more than anything in the world, he had meant what he said: he had not intentionally hurt me, in fact it had hurt him to have to say what he did.

He shattered me but at the same time our meeting was the catalyst which finally threw me into the arms of Jesus because, at that point in my life, there had been nowhere else to go.

(*)   The full story of my abortion is told in:
       ABORTION: A WOMAN'S BIRTHRIGHT?

Like Job, I was lying helpless and defenceless at the bottom of a deep dark pit, plagued with guilt and despair and imagining that I had been abandoned by all those I loved. It was only then that I found time to listen to Jesus. His voice is so gentle that it's easy to ignore it, and I'd ignored it for forty years, going mechanically through the motions of being a Christian without knowing the freedom and the joy which only total surrender to Him can bring.

Although I did not know it then, God had had His hand on my life throughout those forty years and He was gradually drawing all the strands together whilst still giving me my free will to make my own decisions, rather like a toddler on a set of reins. The child is able to run everywhere, to dart here and there; he is given the chance to choose his own direction and yet, all the time, loving hands are loosely, yet firmly, on those reins, not forcing him on to any one path but gently guiding him, not preventing his falls but lifting him up afterwards and, occasionally, jerking him away from danger. That was how God had been holding on to me during those long years when I sought Him yet never really found Him.

But it was not until I stopped striving, trying to do things in my own strength instead of handing over my burden to Him and allowing Him to work through me, that I realised that Jesus had been there all the time, gently knocking at the door of my heart, longing for me to open it and give Him permission to come in and clean up the mess I had made of my life, and take His rightful place as my Lord and Saviour. (*)

When I at last surrendered my life to Him, Jesus didn't immediately give me all the answers I was seeking. He didn't solve the problem of pain in the twinkling of an eye, but He gently led me through the dark valley, lifted me out of the well of despair and showed me that nothing had happened in my life by accident. He hadn't instigated the pain but He had guided me through it and nothing, least of all my suffering, need be wasted because He was able to use every situation for

(*)   The full story of my conversion is told in
       EYE OF THE STORM

good, bring good even out of evil, out of suffering, if only I would allow Him.

And I ended by thanking God for bringing Stephen into my life, for the pain knowing Stephen had caused me because, through those precious weeks with him, Jesus had taught me that whenever we love there is always an element of pain and yet, without love, our life is hollow and meaningless: that suffering is indeed part of life and inevitable if we want to know the ecstasy, the inexplicable joy, of loving another human being.

I realise now that God had put out signposts for me to follow all along the way, but I had so often remained under the signpost, rather than going on to find out where it was leading. How stupid we would think a person who sees an arrow reading 'Paris' and who, although longing to know Paris, merely sits down by the arrow and goes no further. Yet that is what I had done, and what I'm afraid many people are still doing in their search for the truth. Jesus teaches that however far we go in this life, the best is yet to come; we must not stop at the signpost but go on until we reach the real thing, the place to which it is pointing.

· Now looking back over the years I see how God has skilfully woven the threads of my life into the tapestry He has designed. Unfortunately, down here we only see the underside with the knots and the joins, and until we see the completed work right side up, we can have no idea what the finished tableau of our lives will be.

God brought Jane to me at a time when I needed to understand that I was not alone in my pain, that other people were hurting too. And through her that flimsy veil which hides Him from us began to lift for me.

Jacques' visit came when I so desperately needed to talk to someone I could trust, someone who was right out of the picture, not someone I saw every day nor someone who had advised me against becoming a nurse but someone who knew me well and had not been involved in all the discussions. Jacques was just right; he listened and above all he encouraged me. Was God looking even further into the future at that moment, He who can see the beginning from the end, and keeping our friendship alive until the time when I would finally arrive in Paris and meet him again?

⟩ Could that chance meeting with Liz on Westminster Bridge

have been merely a coincidence?

I don't think so.

God was there that Sunday afternoon, at another crossroads in my life, and He offered me a path to follow. He in no way influenced me or obliged me to take that path; the choice was entirely mine, but He gave me the opportunity to accept it or to reject it and seek another way.

During the whole of my nursing training I only once shared a room. I cannot think it was pure coincidence that it happened at a time when I so desperately needed Judy's gentle loving friendship, her deep faith and commitment, to help me keep my balance during that crisis in my life.

Yet that was not the only crisis which her friendship helped me to weather, when her strong faith was there for me to lean on. When I returned to the hospital for my abortion Judy was the Sister of the ward to which I was admitted. She was there beside me at that bleak raw period when I so needed a hand to grasp, a sure faith to uphold me.

Strangely enough, the only other member of the nursing staff whom I recognised from my nursing days at that time was Night Sister.

I was standing dithering outside Matron's office, bewildered by all the changes which had taken place at the hospital since I left, when she approached me and greeted me so warmly that I had the impression that she was genuinely pleased to see me. As we stood chatting together like two old friends delighted to be reunited, I was able to tell her how much she had taught me and to thank her for those lessons of discipline and devotion which she had not only instilled into us all but put into practice in her own life.

When we parted her face, now showing signs of age, was softened by emotion and, seeing tears glistening in those steel-grey eyes, I realised for the first time that, like Miss Balfour, she also must once have been a very attractive woman.

Since we had last met, the bomb damage and the gaping hole open to the sky which had once been a freezing feature of the hospital's long main corridor had disappeared, and in the intervening years been replaced by a shining new wing. But I was lost in this bright unfamiliar modern structure and it was Night Sister who took me gently by the arm and guided me to the department where I had my appointment with a consultant.

The consultant turned out to be Simon, from those far-off Annexe days, whom I had linked up with later in my training when I had often made him a cup of hot cocoa at three o'clock in the morning after calling him out to an emergency in the ward. Meeting him again and laughing and chatting together over old times helped to break the mounting dread and tension inside me and bring a semblance of temporary peace to my shredded nerves and my ravaged mind.

And a week later when Judy walked beside the trolley as I was wheeled into the theatre ante-room prior to my operation a green-gowned figure, his face almost entirely obscured by a mask, said pleasantly: "Hallo Bertie."

"It's Adrian," Judy smiled, as he took my arm and felt for the vein.

Adrian, who had been 'going in for anaesthetics' when he so deftly changed the records for us at our Scottish dancing sessions, 'just happened' to be on duty that afternoon, and administered my anaesthetic.

Now that I am in the autumn of my life and can look back on this whole series of events which took place when I was in my twenties, I cannot believe that they happened by chance. I can only believe that a loving God was always there beside me – although for the first forty years of my life I did not acknowledge His presence. And although I broke His commandment by destroying the child He had given me, He still loved me so unconditionally that, in spite of everything, He forgave me and guided me through this traumatic time with these outward signs of His love.

And even though, after all these years of being a Christian, suffering still often baffles and angers me and sometimes defeats me, yet I know that it was the suffering and not the 'good times' which brought me still further along the road. Suffering honed me, moulded me and burned away the dross; it changed me from the proud, arrogant, rather self-centred young woman I once was and made me into the person I now am: someone whom God is still working on, someone who still has a long way to go but someone who has found peace and been able to come to terms with life on earth, content to leave her future and the future of those she loves in His hands.

Jesus has shown me that He is not only WITH us in our suffering but that He UNDERSTANDS our suffering, because He himself suffered. Did He not say, "My soul is overwhelmed with sorrow" when He was facing the pain of humiliation and rejection which ended at the cross?

We do not have an aloof God but a compassionate Saviour who understands. He has proved to me Jane's words that His Kingdom is characterised by hope. This is not a sop to our present sufferings, but an extension of them into the place where the joys of this life will not be cancelled but fulfilled by death, where there will be no more death or mourning or crying or pain, where He will wipe every tear from our eyes.

His Kingdom, the hope of glory, gives our suffering context and perspective, however much it may hurt at the time, because the Bible teaches us that earthly suffering, however deep, will not last but God's Kingdom will last forever.

Through my contact with suffering, as a nurse, then as a mother, as an ordinary human being, I have discovered that whatever happens God loves us with a steadfast, everlasting love. Even though we may change, and our lives be turned upside down and inside out, Jesus never changes: He is the same yesterday, today and forever.

Although I still don't have a clear-cut answer to the great mystery of life's pain and injustices – if I did I would be God – I'm not pining to know it all down here: I'm content to wait till I get to heaven, to His Kingdom, and meet Him face to face because like Jane, like Stephen, like Judy, I now have HIM and THAT is what makes the difference. I know that I am a dearly loved child of God, a member of His Royal Family, and like each one of his children, unique and precious in His sight. I know that even before the world was created He chose me for a purpose and, in His time, all will be revealed.

And knowing this, secure in this, I have discovered that there are really very few questions in life, suffering being certainly one of them, but they can all be answered by three little words which Jesus spoke to His disciples:

Come to me.

"Come to me all you who are weary and burdened, and I will give you rest." (Matthew 11 v.28) (NIV)

EPILOGUE

I have known pain and I've known sorrow,
And I've known times when life seemed
hard to bear,
I've known emptiness of soul, when I
couldn't find a friend
But above it all, I've known Jesus.

I've known depression, when tears ran
down my face,
When I looked around for comfort, no
one there,
I've known bitterness within, when I
grieved my Lord,
But above it all I've known Jesus.

In this I have security,
That Jesus knows my way,
And though it all seems dark sometimes
With Him it's bright as day.
In Him I place my confidence,
I trust all to His love,
For above it all, I've known Jesus.

Lines from a chorus which came out of war-torn
Northern Ireland: the author is unknown to me. I include
this as a tribute and as an echo to the thoughts and
experiences I have endeavoured to share in these pages.

For further details of Word products please complete coupon below.

Books ☐

Word Records – Cassettes ☐

Lifelifter Cassettes ☐

Video ☐

Please tick items of interest

Name...

Address..

....

....

Word Publishing
Word (UK) Ltd
9 Holdom Avenue, Bletchley, Milton Keynes.
MK1 1QU

HEALING AND WHOLENESS
Dr. Robert Baldwin

Why sickness?

Is there a remedy?

Why am I not healed?

These and other questions are covered in this
timely book by a Christian doctor and pastor.
Chapters on depression, guilt, anxiety and
bereavement give counsel both to sufferers and
those seeking to help them. As a pastor who has
seen people healed, Dr. Baldwin stresses the
importance of prayer, praise and the gifts of the
Spirit in making healing a reality — but emphasizes
at all times the need for compassion and sensitivity,
and closes with a message of encouragement to
those who have not known healing.

Dr. Robert Baldwin, MB, BCh, worked in General
Practice in South Wales for five years. He is now
pastor of The Gospel Tabernacle in Pontllanfraith, a
thriving church in the Welsh Valleys, where he lives
with his wife Sharon and three young children.

Catalogue No. YB9168 £2.75

RUNNING ON EMPTY
Jill Briscoe

refilling your spirit at the low points of life

A BOOK FOR ANYONE who has ever felt depressed, frustrated, sad, unloved, guilty — or just plain tired!

For those times in life when your resources are almost depleted — when you're out of energy with miles to go and no relief in sight — Jill Briscoe offers a fresh word of hope and comfort.

She points out that even the great characters of the Bible had their low points —
* ELIJAH, who was drained in doing God's work
* LEAH, who was ugly and unloved
* DAVID, who was faced with the temptation of a beautiful woman
* HANNAH, who was middle-aged and unfulfilled
* JONAH, who was on the run from God
* THE PRODIGAL SON, whose good time had turned bad
* MARTHA, who had no help and too much to do
* MOSES, who was burning out with people problems
* NAOMI, who was bitter with grief
* HABBAKUK, who wondered where God was in the hard times

— but God brought each of them refreshment and renewal. And with her usual insight and humour, Jill Briscoe shows that such refreshment and renewal is available to any of us — even when we are running on empty.

JILL BRISCOE was born in England and attended Homerton College in Cambridge. She is involved in the ministry of Elmbrook Church in Wisconsin where her husband Stuart is senior pastor. A popular speaker and author, she is the mother of three children and has two grandchildren.

Catalogue No. YB9309 £2.75

FACING DEATH
AND THE LIFE AFTER

Billy Graham

If we want to make the most of life, we need to face the fact that it is going to end, says Dr. Graham at the beginning of this book. He goes on to discuss the many issues raised by the inevitability of death, including:

Coping with Grief ★ The Death of Children
Life as a Preparation for Death ★ Euthanasia
Dying with Dignity ★ Sharing the Grief of Others
Moving from Terror to Acceptance

Billy Graham's undoubted skills as a communicator are put to excellent use in this positive and practical book . . . Of particular help for those counselling the dying and the bereaved.

21st Century Christian

This is the book every pastor should read . . . A timely book for these troubled times.

Good News

If all books about the last times were as relevant as this the church would be greatly blessed.

Harvester

Catalogue Number YB 9133   £2.95